ONE HUNE
TO CHANGE YOUR LIFE

Pierre Lefèvre

ONE HUNDRED STORIES TO CHANGE YOUR LIFE

Small tales in answer to large questions

 St Paul Publications

St Paul Publications
Middlegreen, Slough SL3 6BT, United Kingdom

English translation copyright © St Paul Publications UK 1991

ISBN 085439 382 X

Printed by The Guernsey Press Co. Ltd., Guernsey, C.I.

St Paul Publications is an activity of the priests and brothers of the Society of St Paul who proclaim the Gospel through the media of social communication

Contents

Acknowledgements: I should like to thank my former colleagues Gertrud Rieger and Günther Grimme for their help and encouragement; Sr Gertrud Bischof for the faultless typescript; Mary Todd and Paula Burckhardt who made this text possible by freeing me from many daily chores; the many teenagers for their suggestions and selections of short stories.

Foreword

Can we learn from life?

A cat can. A cat will jump on the hotplate once but not twice.

The Italians say: 'Experience is the best teacher. Pity it often comes too late.' Our own experience usually comes too late. But we can learn from the experience of others.

Others' experience however carries more weight when it is recounted in such a way that it is *relived*. Hence these small tales in answer to large questions.

This book falls into two parts: *Being Human* and *Being Christian*.

Being Human deals with the four most important human virtues, namely justice, prudence, fortitude and temperance. It is also useful as a lesson in ethics and morals.

Being Christian gives an introduction to our faith (the Creed, the Our Father, the Ten Commandments, the Sacraments) and is chiefly directed to groups and families.

Finally there is love (of God and of neighbour) and that is for everyone.

BEING HUMAN

Justice

'That's not fair.'

How often we hear this from students comparing marks, footballers complaining about the referee, office workers when they get their pay packets.

And so it is remarkable how everyone is against injustice . . . and therefore in favour of justice.

But justice is more than getting one's due. It consists above all in being willing to give others their due.

1. What is justice?

It means: giving others their due.

Truth is not to be bought

Chosroes, the Persian emperor, had against all expectations recovered from his severe illness. So he called his counsellors together and said: 'I should like to know from you what you expect of me. Do you think I am a good emperor? Speak the truth without fear. In return I should like to make each of you the present of a precious stone.'

One after another the counsellors came forward with fine words and exaggerated praise. When it was the turn of the wise Elim he said: 'Sire, I would rather be silent, for truth is not to be bought.'

Then the emperor declared: 'Very well. I shall not give you anything. So, now you can speak your mind.'

Then Elim said: 'Sire, you want to know what I think. I think that you are human, with many weaknesses and failings, just the same as us. But your failings weigh much more heavily for the whole people is groaning under the burden of taxation. I think you are spending too much money on festivities, building palaces, and above all on making war.'

When the emperor heard that, he grew thoughtful. Then he had his counsellors given a jewel each as he had promised. But Elim he named his Prime Minister.

The next day the flatterers came before the emperor. 'Sire,' said their spokesman, 'the dealer who sold you those jewels ought to be hanged. The stones you gave us are false.'

'I know that,' retorted the emperor, 'Yes, indeed, they are false as were your words.'

4

2. How do we know that a person is just and reliable?

By the way in which that person speaks, acts and lives the truth.

Pricking the balloon

A young barrister once rented a magnificent office. To make a dashing impression on all, he had bought a de luxe telephone that for the time being was sitting impressively on his desk waiting to be installed.

A client was announced. The very first.

The young barrister deliberately made him wait for a quarter of an hour. And to create a bigger impression on the client he took the receiver as the man came in, and pretended to be holding a genuine telephone conversation.

'The Director General? . . . My dear sir, we're both only wasting our time. . . Yes, if you absolutely insist. . . But not under ten thousand pounds. All right then, that's settled. . . Goodbye.'

He put the receiver back. The client did in fact seem taken aback by this. Almost confused.

'What can I do for you sir?'

'I. . . I have come to connect your phone.'

Going for gold

The Olympic Games 1928

In Amsterdam the Frenchman Gaudin stood facing an Italian in a fencing match for the gold medal. Both men fought like mad and the onlookers held their breath. The Frenchman was in a difficult position because the tall Italian had a longer reach. Gaudin attacked all the more fiercely and thrust and parry followed one another like lightning.

Suddenly the judges intervened. One thought he had seen the Italian make a hit. Almost a groan went through the crowd. If the Frenchman was hit he had lost the gold medal. . .

5

Now the judges were in agreement. Their spokesman stepped forward: 'No hit.' The onlookers breathed a sigh of relief.

But then the Frenchman tore off his mask. He raised his foil stiffly, took a pace forward towards the judges' stand and announced:

'Je suis touché – a hit.'

The judgement had been in his favour but he would not accept it. Truth meant more to him than a tainted gold medal.

---

3. Where does justice begin?

At home with respect and consideration.

Home politics for a foreign minister

The French foreign minister Robert Schuman was once asked why he had never married.

'A long time ago,' he replied, 'when I was travelling on the underground once, I happened to step on a lady's foot. Before I could apologise she screeched: "Idiot, can't you look where you're putting your big foot!" Then she glanced at me, went red and cried: "Oh please forgive me, I thought it was my husband." '

4. To what does a child have a right above all
else?

**To parents who stay together and bring their
child up with love and firmness.**

A terror

A midwife who had assisted at childbirths for forty years
has the following reminiscences:

Done at last! At butcher Smith's a boy had come into
the world. The father was beside himself over the child, his
boy Tiny Tim. Any child going past his shop was given a
sausage.

Meanwhile the baby was yelling. From the first he was
a little terror in the home. He wanted to sleep during the
day, and at night he had to be carried from room to room
to stop him bawling. I raised a protest.

'Bring your boy up sensibly. Get him used early on to
being obedient and tidy. Do everything he wants and you'll
bring the child up for the reformatory.'

The mother would have none of it. 'Once he's old enough
to understand he'll stop his naughtiness. You have to give
a child freedom to develop.'

After about a year Mrs Smith called me in as I was passing by. There was Tiny Tim sitting on his potty in the middle
of the table. He had his mother's scissors in his hands and
was sliding to and fro on his throne and cutting off the buds
and leaves of the plants in the window.

'And then you eat off that table afterwards!' I couldn't
help remarking.

'What can I do? He won't stay sitting if he can't get to
the window. . .'

I took the scissors from the little lad's hands. 'If he pokes
his eye out with them, Mrs Smith. . .'

So then the little rogue went scarlet in the face, clenched
both fists, stamped his feet, shouted and raged.

'Yes' the father laughed, 'the boy has something in him.
He's got guts and won't put up with anything.'

7

And the mother made excuses. 'He cries until he gets what he wants. What can you do. . . I give it to him to keep him quiet. As soon as he's old enough to understand it will be different. He's still so small. . .'

I had seized the little man somewhat vigorously by his woolly without saying anything and sat him on his throne on the ground. 'Either you're quiet and do your business. . .' and I glared at him. Struck dumb and rigid he crouched there. . . did not dare utter a whimper at such unwonted treatment. . . looked round to father and mother for help. But they were quite as floored as he and the mother found a way out: 'It's easy too see you have no children or you couldn't be like that with him. He's still so small and hasn't any sense yet. . .'

What I would have liked to say to that was: 'Just like you.' But I held my tongue and went. All that for nothing!

Once the family was sitting in the back room having a meal. 'Don't want it,' bawled Tiny Tim and slung his plate full of soup onto the floor. His father laughed: 'He's a terror, our little Tiny Tim.'

Oh yes he was a terror, and more so every day. All the children ran from him when he was in the street. Soon he was tormenting little chickens. 'Oh they're only animals,' said his father.

Tiny Tim went to school. He was a stubborn and deceitful playmate and no one was safe from his tricks. As he could not be openly nasty there he was all the more beastly on the sly. His teacher repeatedly tried to have him sent to a home for difficult children. But nobody wanted to upset Tiny Tim and it never came off.

One fine day father and son came to blows. After the thirteen-year-old horror had already gone through the whole contents of the till in the morning he tried to take the safe key in the afternoon. That was too much for his old father. 'That belongs to me so long as I'm master here. Get it?' Thereupon the lad in a rage seized hold of a meatcleaver and struck out at his father. He missed. But Mr Smith stood there as though hit by lightning. Then all at once his eyes were opened. And at that moment ungovernable rage gripped him too. For the first time he took hold of the boy and gave him a hiding, with neither rhyme nor reason of course. He would certainly have beaten him to death if the mother and the apprentices had not come between them. The Smith household was shaken. Tiny Tim lay in bed for a week.

The father had made a thorough job of it. But it was too late. This sudden change-round only brought out in the lad the vengefulness, malice and brutality which had been lurking under the surface. And hate stepped in.

Some months later he really did strike his father with the cleaver. The place was in an uproar. Such a thing had never been seen in living memory. And yet . . . and yet . . . they all saw and felt it: the father and mother had brought disaster on themselves.

Many parents took account then that bringing up children is no easy task and an important undertaking, and that it is no good waiting until 'They are old enough to understand'.

---

5. How are we to act justly towards subordinates?

By giving each their due without preference.

Misuse of power

I passed my childhood in Ireland. In class 3 of the National school we had a very strict teacher. He was called McSweeney.

While he was in class McSweeney often had visits from acquaintances. Each time he went out to the corridor and talked endlessly. But before leaving the classroom he appointed his favourite, Paddy, to be in charge of the class.

Paddy was a sturdy red-haired boy, and sat in the back row. His task in the absence of the teacher was to write the names of offenders on the blackboard. And there you were with a whole list of names written up in a trice. Then the dealing began. One of his victims whose name had gone on the board would beg for mercy.

'Rub my name out and I'll give you a sweet.'

'No it must be at least three sweets.'

'The most I'll give is two.'

'Two's not enough.'

'All right then, three.'

Other miscreants had apples, chocolates, glass marbles to offer. Real 'criminals' had to get out of it with a pocket knife, sling or even a water pistol.

Then when the dreaded teacher rather suddenly came back there were only three or four names still on the blackboard. These were poor boys who had nothing and so could not buy themselves off. They regularly received a number of strokes. There were often bitter tears.

That was a shock for me. For the first time I experienced how the rich are privileged. And it was not the last time.

---

6. How do I act justly towards superiors?

By observing their directions for the common good.

A cunning apology

In 1981 the editor of a newspaper was fined £20,000. He had defamed the good name of the writer Heinrich Böll.

In the nineteenth century it was possible to get off more cheaply. The actor Beckmann had called a journalist 'the biggest fool in town'. For that the judge condemned him to go to the home of the injured party and beg his pardon before witnesses.

At the appointed hour the journalist was waiting with his friends in his lodging for Beckmann to come and apologise.

They did not have long to wait. The doorbell rang. Beckmann put his head round the half-opened door and asked:

'Does Schultz live here?'

The journalist replied, somewhat taken aback, 'No, not here.'

'Oh my apologies', said Beckmann. . . and disappeared.

---

7. What do the world's poorest have to suffer from?

From hunger, lack of education, and racial discrimination.

A black makes good

Martin Luther King is celebrated for being in the forefront of the fight for Black Civil Rights. Less well known is the great negro leader and educationalist Booker Washington.

Booker Washington was a small negro boy when Abraham Lincoln was President of the U.S.A. Even at the age of nine he had to work twelve hours a day in the mines. When Lincoln freed the slaves, this penniless lad decided to attend the Hampton School, one of the few schools for blacks. Let us hear his own account of his 800 kilometre journey to school.

'My first night on the way I shall never forget. We were wending our way through the mountains of Virginia in an old stage coach. In the evening we stopped at a wayside inn. The other travellers were whites. After they had been shown their rooms and were waiting for a meal I went timidly up to the landlord. In truth I had hardly any money but the night was very cold and so I hoped to be given shelter all the same. I said: "Please sir, I should like a room."

'The landlord looked at me outraged: "No room here for dirty niggers."

'Somehow I managed to keep warm through the long night. That was the first time I experienced for myself the difference skin colour makes.

'After a few days on foot and begging lifts I reached the town of Richmond, which was still 150 kilometres from my goal, Hampton. I was tired, hungry and dirty when I arrived there late at night, without a penny in my pocket and not knowing where to go.

'I tried at various doors but all wanted money. Not knowing what to do I turned off from one street into another and as I did so came upon an old eating house temptingly offering roast chicken and apple pudding. It seemed to me I would have gladly paid out a fortune for a taste of them. But I had nothing and so had nothing to eat.

'As soon as it was day I saw a great ship nearby. It was unloading old iron. I went straight over and asked the captain to be allowed to help with the unloading so as to earn something to eat. I was fearfully hungry. The captain, a white man of friendly aspect, showed understanding.

'I worked until I had enough to get breakfast and never before or since has a breakfast tasted better.

'After two weeks I succeeded in reaching Hampton School. I went straight to the Mistress of the School to present myself. After so many days without regular food, a bath or a change of clothes, I of course made a bad impression. She refused to take me.

'As I remained stubbornly before the door she said to me after some hours: "That classroom over there wants sweeping. Here's a broom."

'I saw it as a chance of a lifetime. I cleared out the room three times with the broom. Then I found a rag and dusted round four times. When I had finished I reported back to the head teacher. She was a yankee from the north and knew well enough where to look for any dust. She examined floor and cupboards. She took out her handkerchief and passed it over the tables and benches. Not finding the least trace of dust anywhere in the room she said quietly: "Okay, we'll take you on trial."

'I was the happiest person on earth.

'I had to work hard to pay for my schooling and board. At four in the morning I began lighting up the stoves. Then I got ready for school. In the evening I cleaned classrooms until late into the night. It was hard, very hard.

'But I made it.'

8. What are the causes of violence, terrorism and war?

Insatiable greed for possessions and power, and the anger of the oppressed in consequence.

The vicious circle of violence

The Puerto Rican Nicky Cruz tells of his school days in New York:

'Lessons were over. I was walking alone across the school yard and was aware of some boys following me. I looked back over my shoulder. Behind me were five black boys and a girl. I knew that there had already been plenty of pitched battles between blacks and Puerto Ricans. So I walked faster but heard them quicken their pace as well.

'I left the yard and went along the path to the road. The young blacks caught up with me and one of them, a hefty lad, pushed me against the wall. I dropped my books and another pushed them into the gutter which had water in it.

'I looked round but could see no one I could call to for help. "What are you doing on our beat, little 'un?" asked the boy. "Don't you know this is our beat?"

' "This is the school, man. It doesn't belong to any gang."

' "Don't you believe it, little 'un," countered the other. "I don't like you." He put a hand on my chest and pushed me up against the wall. At that instant I heard a click and knew it for the sound of a flick-knife.

'The big boy put the point of the knife against my chest and tapped my shirt buttons. "Watch out what happens, my boy," he said. "You're still new here and when you're new you need protection, d'you follow? You pay me 25 cents a day and no one does anything to you."

'One of the other boys sniggered and added: "Yes we'll do it so good we won't do anything to you ourselves you see."

'The others laughed.

' "So," I said "if I really give you 25 cents a day what

13

guarantee do I have then that you'll really leave me alone?''

' ''None whatever, you sly little thing, because you give it to us whether or no. Otherwise we do you in,'' answered the big boy.

' ''All right then you'd best do me in right away. Otherwise I'll finish you off one after the other.'' I saw clearly that the others were already feeling somewhat worried. The big boy who was holding the knife at my chest thought I was right-handed so he wasn't expecting it when I suddenly seized his arm with my left hand, pushed him away from my chest and threw him on his back. He let the knife fall and I picked it up. It felt good in my hand. Then I pressed his face against the wall with the knifepoint close under his ear. A girl screamed.

'I turned to her. ''Hey, Baby! I know you! I know where you live. This evening I'll come and do you in. How'd you like that?'' She screamed even louder, seized hold of one of the other boys and tried to drag him away. ''Run,'' she screamed, ''that boy's mad! Run!''

'They ran away. And the big boy too that had pushed me against the wall with his knife.

'I went to the gutter where my books were, picked them out and brushed off the water. I still had the knife in my hand. I slipped it into my jacket pocket and went home. From now on, I reflected, they'll think twice before taking up with Nicky.'

Nicky Cruz didn't let the knife rest in his pocket. Driven on by hate and vengeance he became one of the most dangerous gang leaders in New York. . . until David Wilkerson led him to Christ.

14

9. Does the state have first right to the education of children?

No, it belongs to the parents in the first place.

Dictatorship on trial

'Police!' came the frightened cry of a child in warning. Like the wind the seven children rushed from the house, clambered over the fence and were gone.

The police officer greeted Madame Trofim politely. Behind him an official entered and came straight to the point: 'By decree of the city people's court the father's parental rights are withdrawn. And we are taking the children now. Where are they?'

Their father was in custody for preaching. For this reason his children were to be forced to go into a home where they would hear nothing of Christ.

'You have no right,' countered Madame Trofim, 'my parental rights as the mother have not been withdrawn. As the mother, I have all rights over the children and I will not give them up.'

'Very well. We'll take care of that. We will withdraw your parental rights too,' came the cold reply. Then the police went back to debate the case in court. One policeman who stayed behind suddenly noticed something moving behind the wooden fence; questioning children's eyes were peering through the cracks.

'Come on quick, into the house,' he ordered.

But they took off like a flurry of sparrows, scattering in different directions to the hiding place they had themselves prepared by the cemetery. As the police could not find the children either in the street or in the neighbouring house they went away.

When it began to grow dark and the children were still not back the grandmother went in search of them.

'Nana, have they gone?' a little voice asked suddenly. One of the children had been sent out to reconnoitre.

'Yes, my cherub! Run and call the others.'

With a mixture of caution and triumph on their faces the children returned home. And there was thanksgiving to God for keeping them safe. The police did not come again.

These children were lucky. We know how many other children in Russia were snatched away from their parents for reasons of religion.

---

10. What is freedom of religion?

Freedom from state intervention in religious matters.

The forbidden book

Ivan was an evangelical Christian shut away in a Russian concentration camp for his missionary activities.

While he was still free he had made preparations to carry on his mission in the camp, filling a small notebook with texts from the Bible.

But how was he to smuggle his little book into the camp? Everything was strictly controlled. The new detainees had to range themselves along the wall of a large empty room. One after the other they were searched to the skin and then sent over to the other side of the room.

Ivan had thought of an extremely daring plan. He hid his little book under his foot. Suddenly a man collapsed. It was an elderly Christian pretending to faint. So for an instant the attention of the guards was distracted. Ivan used that instant to send his little book with a good shove sliding across the floor. Like lightning it disappeared again under the foot of a friend on the other side who had been searched already.

So the Word of God entered a communist camp and was for many 'a light for their path' (Psalm 119:105).

Prudence

How do we know a knife is good? Principally because it is sharp.

How do we know a person is good? Above all because that person is just.

So what does a just person aim at? To do what is right by others however hard that may be.

This is justice.

How is it to be done?

By careful consideration to find the right means.

And this is prudence.

11. What is the purpose of prudence?

Prudence considers the means to an end.

He knew how

A sultan had a dream. He dreamed he had lost all his teeth. As soon as he awoke he asked a sage the meaning of the dream. 'Alas, what ill fortune, my lord,' cried the sage. 'Each tooth you lost means the loss of one of your courtiers.' 'What you scoundrel,' yelled the sultan in a rage. 'What do you dare to say to me? Away with him.' And he gave the order: 'Fifty lashes for his impertinence.'

Another sage was summoned and taken before the sultan. When he learned what the dream was he cried: 'What good fortune! What great luck! Our lord and master will outlive all his courtiers.' The sultan's face brightened and he said: 'I thank you, my kind friend. Go straight with my treasurer and let him give you fifty gold pieces.'

On the way the treasurer said to the sage: 'But you did not explain the sultan's dream any differently from the first sage.' With a sly smile the wise man replied: 'Indeed, one can say many things: What is important is how one says them.'

12. What is the difference between justice and prudence?

Justice tells us what to do, prudence tells us how.

New York admits guilt

Of the three-term New York mayor (1933–1945), Fiorello La Guardia, a colourful figure with a flair for the dramatic, the following story is told:

One day he took the place of the police court judge as he occasionally did. It was an icy cold winter's day. A shivering old man was brought before him. The charge: taking a loaf of bread from a bakery.

The accused gave the excuse that his family were starving.

'I have to punish you,' declared La Guardia. 'The law allows of no exceptions. I have to fine you ten dollars.'

But then he felt in his pocket and added: 'Here's ten dollars to pay the fine. And now,' he continued, raising his voice, 'I impose on everyone present in this courtroom a fine of fifty cents – for living in a town where folk must steal bread in order to live – Sergeant, collect the money at once and hand it over to the accused.'

The hat went the rounds and a still half-incredulous man left the court with 47 dollars 50 cents in his pocket.

Should not we too receive punishment, we who have everything, for we live on a small planet where millions of children die of hunger every year.

13. Why is it wise to take advice?

Because no one person, especially a beginner, can know everything.

The whistling lung

A. J. Cronin was at one time a doctor in a Scottish village. Here he narrates an interesting experience of his:

It seemed to me that I was soon being accepted by the village. Maybe I was too successful, as I began to be somewhat conceited sometimes. My senior collegue Dr Cameron would glance critically at me when I appeared to him too sure of my diagnosis.

One afternoon I was sitting in the lab when our cook Janet put her head round the door. 'Something's up at Duncan's. He wants a doctor at once.'

In the hall I found Duncan terribly upset.

'It's the baby,' he said.

'Is it bad?'

'Very bad. The little thing can scarcely breathe. Her lung is whistling frightfully. The district nurse thinks it's pneumonia.'

'Oh, these district nurses,' I thought, 'they always know more than the doctor. Good, we'll go over at once,' I decided.

On arriving at his house we went up to the first floor. I could already hear the child's breathing from the staircase. A laboured, whistling breathing that shocked me. To the mother, half dead with anxiety, I said 'Can you please pull back the curtains a little so that I can see.'

Thereupon the officious district nurse interposed at once: 'I had the curtains drawn. Don't you know strong light is bad for little children?'

'I'm not a cat,' I replied dryly, 'I can't see in the dark.'

The poor little thing, about a year old, was very restless. Her cheeks were red and swollen, she tossed to and fro, wailed heartrendingly, held onto the bed clothes, clutched her face — and all the time that awful whistling breath. I took her temperature: 37.5. Then I listened to her chest, which was awfully difficult because she threw herself about all the time.

I didn't know what to think. That whistling breathing couldn't come from pneumonia. It was something I had never met before. I was worried, very worried. But so as not to stand there mute I said: 'It's the lung.'

'The lung,' repeated the nurse and raised her eyes heavenward. 'As if I didn't know that already. Tell us instead what is to be done before the little treasure whistles to death.'

'Do nothing,' I said, furious, for I was well acquainted with the district nurse's impossible remedies. 'I'm coming straight back. I must consult Dr Cameron.'

'That's the most sensible thing you've said since you came in,' the old woman said.

I found Dr Cameron at his tea. 'Now, then what's up? You seem a bit excited.'

'A whistling lung,' I answered.

Cameron's eyebrows went up. 'Never heard of it.'

'Then you're going to hear it now,' I replied grimly.

A short while later we were with the child. Cameron took the little one carefully from the cradle and pressed his ear against the small chest. Suddenly it seemed to me he smiled, or was it the effect of the light playing on his weather-beaten face?

He turned to the mother: 'Have you a hairpin, my dear — or something of the sort?'

'A hairpin?' she stammered disbelieving and reached for her bun.

'That's right,' he confirmed with a nod. 'And now you can leave me alone with my colleague. We have something to discuss.' Torn between anxiety and astonishment Mrs Duncan left quietly.

'You too!' Cameron ordered the nurse curtly.

'It will be best if I stay. Perhaps I can help.'

Cameron's face darkened. 'Out!' he shouted, 'and quickly or you'll get my boot in your fat backside.'

That was too much even for the hardboiled district nurse. She screamed and ran out of the room.

Cameron gave a smile. 'Isn't it amazing what can't be done with kindness? By the way young man, d'you know what a squeaker is?'

'A squeaker,' I repeated, baffled.

'Exactly. A squeaker. That's what I said.'

I stared at him.

'Well,' said Cameron, 'I will tell you what it is. A squeaker is a tiny button which squeaks when you blow in it. Children play with them and babies like stuffing them in their ears, mouth and up their nostrils even.' As he spoke he bent over the cradle, the hairpin in his hand. Quickly and gently he pushed the hairpin into the child's nostril and drew it out. The whistling breathing stopped at once.

'Good Lord!' I burst out.

'There's your whistling lung,' Cameron remarked softly, holding out the little whistle on his palm.

The baby smiled engagingly at Cameron, pulled up her little legs and began playing with her toes. I went scarlet, murmuring shamefacedly that I was the biggest fool in the world. I put out my hand to take the whistle. But Cameron dropped it in an inside pocket. 'No my boy,' he said in a friendly tone. 'That stays safe with me. And the next time I notice you getting a bit above yourself I'll be dead sure to produce it.'

---

14. Why is prudence called foresight?

Because it can foresee difficulties ahead and act accordingly.

'Mummy why. . . ?'

'Mummy, why won't you play with me?' asked seven-year-old Nelly.

'Because I haven't time.'

'Why haven't you time?'

'Because I'm working.'

'Why are you working?'

'To earn money.'

'Why do you earn money?'

'To get you something to eat.'

'Oh, but I'm not hungry, Mummy!'

15. What can a wise person learn from a rogue?

Imagination and an understanding of humanity — essential for wise dealing.

'Love conquers'

The writer Peter Axworthy's first novel bore the title *Love conquers*. Unfortunately nobody bought it. The book remained on the booksellers' shelves.

But Axworthy knew what to do. He had the following notice inserted in several of the big newspapers:
'Millionaire, aged 30, well set up, sporting, music lover, wants to marry a girl just like the heroine of the novel *Love conquers.*'

The result was not long in coming. All the copies of the book were sold out by the end of the week.

16. Why is it often wise to listen to the young when making a decision?

Because youth often finds a bold new way out.

Nothing to be done

Copenhagen, 13 November 1953.

In the fire brigade's call centre the telephone rings. It is 3 a.m. Erik, the young fireman on night duty, takes up the receiver. He is 22.

'Fire brigade here. . .'

No reply. But he hears heavy breathing. And then an agitated woman's voice:

'Help, help! I can't get up. I'm in a pool of blood.'

'Keep calm, we're coming straight away. Where are you?'

'I don't know.'

'Are you at home?'

'Yes. I think so at least.'

'Where is it, what street?'

'I don't know. I'm dizzy. I'm losing blood.'

'Well tell me your name.'

'I can't remember anything. I must have banged my head.'

'Stay by the phone please.' Erik goes to a second phone and dials the exchange. A man's voice replies.

'Can you, please,' says Erik, 'give me the number of the person calling the fire brigade just now?'

'No I can't. I'm the night watchman and don't know anything about technical things. And today being Saturday the right people are not around.'

Erik hangs up. Then an idea strikes him. He asks the woman: 'How did you manage to find the fire brigade number?'

'It's written on the phone. I must have taken it with me as I fell.'

'Have a look to see whether your number isn't on it.'

'No there's nothing else on it. But please come quickly.' The voice is getting weaker.

'Tell me, what can you see from where you are?'

'I can see. . . I can see windows and the street lamps outside.'

Aha, thinks Erik, she lives on the street side and can't be higher up than the 3rd floor if she can see the lamps.

'What sort of window is it?' he inquires again. 'Is it square?'

'No it's a long one.'

So, thinks Erik, she must be living in a downtown area.

'Is there a light in your room?'

'Yes, the light's on.'

Erik wants to ask more but there is no reply.

Time is passing. What can he do?

From the nearby fire station Erik rings up the fire brigade chief. He puts the problem to him. The chief's opinion is:

'Nothing to be done there. We can't possibly find the woman. And besides,' he complains, 'the fire brigade main line is being occupied meanwhile by this woman. Supposing there's a fire somewhere.'

24

Erik refuses to give up. During his training he was taught that a fireman's first duty is to save lives.

Suddenly he has a wild idea and tells his chief.

But the captain is taken aback.

'That's mad! People will think there's been an atom bomb. In the middle of the night in a town with a million inhabitants!'

'Please,' begs Erik, 'we must act quickly before it is too late.'

Silence at the other end of the line. Then Erik hears: 'All right we'll do it. I'll be right over.'

A quarter of an hour later twenty small fire brigade vehicles are out in the old part of the town with sirens wailing. Each one has a certain district to quarter.

The woman gives no further sign but Erik can hear her breathing. After ten minutes Erik calls: 'Now I can hear a siren through the receiver!'

Straight away the captain speaks on his intercom:

'Car no. 1. Shut off your siren.' He refers to Erik.

'I can still hear the siren,' says the young man.

'Car no. 2. Shut off your siren.'

At the twelfth car Erik says in triumph: 'The siren has stopped now.'

The captain gives the order on the radio: 'Car no. 12 put your siren on again.'

Erik informs him: 'I can hear it again but now it's fainter.'

'Car no. 12. Turn round,' says the captain.

Shortly afterwards from Erik: 'It's getting louder, it's quite loud, it must be in the street.'

'Car no. 12. Look to see which window has a light showing.'

A growl comes back: 'Hundreds of lights on. They're all at their windows!'

'Use your loudhailer,' orders the captain.

Erik hears the loudspeaker through the telephone: 'Ladies and gentlemen, we are looking for a woman in danger of her life. Her light is on. Please put your lights out.'

The lights go out, only one window remains alight. Shortly after Erik can hear the door being broken open; then a man's voice comes over the phone: 'She's unconscious but her pulse is still beating. We're taking her straight to the hospital. I think she'll manage.'

Ellen Thorndall – that was her name – did in fact manage. She recovered consciousness. Even her memory returned after a few weeks.

---

17. Why does experience help us to do the right thing?

Because it teaches us the consequences of our actions.

Can you keep silence?

During the American Civil War, General Jackson was addressed by an enquirer: 'May I ask, General, when you intend to attack the enemy?'

Whereupon the General whispered in his ear: 'Tell me, can you keep a secret?'

'Yes of course, General. . .'

To which Jackson replied: 'So can I.' And left the self-important person standing.

---

18. What are the signs of imprudence?

Insufficient attention, thoughtless decisions, indecisive action.

Pity about that

Wilhelminer Schröder, a famous actress and singer, was already past her prime. One day she was travelling from Hamburg to Frankfurt in a first class carriage. The conversation turned on herself. A lady declared that Ms Schröder's voice had much gone off, her future as a star was over. She had gone as podgy as a fatted goose.

A gentleman sitting beside her overhearing this criticism, suggested with a smile: 'You can say that to the singer herself because she happens to be sitting opposite to you.'

The lady paled and stammered a string of apologies. At last she came upon a saving excuse: 'My stupid remarks madam,' she said to the actress, 'are certainly the fault of the journalist in the evening paper. One can never trust in his poisonous theatre reviews. A dreadful man that journalist.'

The actress replied sweetly: 'Won't you tell him so yourself? . . . He's sitting right beside you.'

---

19. Is prudence to be found in reflection or rather in the decision?

What is important is to carry out resolutely a well-considered decision.

The hiding-place

Anne Frank was not the only one of the many Jews who had to go underground in Holland.

Corrie ten Boom tells how her house in Haarlem became a refuge for Jews on the run. She lived with her father and her sister Betsie over the family clock-maker's business.

The Jews in Haarlem had many friends. One who was an architect, Mr Smith, came to see Corrie. He was shocked when he learned that there was no secret room in the house. He declared himself ready to construct a hiding-place for her Jewish friends.

'The hiding-place must be situated as high up as possible,' was the architect's opinion. 'That gives the Jews time to reach it while the search is going on below.'

Corrie continues her account:

He came to my room at the top of the stairs and called out happily: 'That's the place.'

'But. . .' I stammered, 'this is my bedroom.'

Mr Smith paid no attention. He was already measuring it up and dragging the old wardrobe away from the wall.

'That's where the dummy wall will go. I dare not make the space any wider,' he said. 'But it will be enough for a camp-bed. Oh yes, that's fine.'

The next day he and his workmen kept coming in and out. They never knocked. Each time they came each one brought something in. Tools folded in a newspaper. A few bricks in a suitcase. 'What! Wood?' he cried when I ventured to ask whether it would not be easier to put up a wooden partition. 'Wood rings hollow. They'll hear straight away that there's a space behind. No, no, bricks are the only possibility for a dummy wall.'

After the wall had been put up the plasterer came, the carpenter, and finally the decorator. Six days after work began, Mr Smith called in Betsie, Father and me to inspect.

We stood at the door and stared. All four walls were as flecked and smutty as all the rooms in Haarlem, where coal was used for heating. Old water stains covered the back wall, a wall I could scarcely believe to have been brought in, seventy-five centimetres away from the real wall. Built-in bookcases ran the whole length of the dummy wall. In the left-hand corner at the bottom under the lowest shelf was a fifty-centimetre sliding door which could be pushed up. Mr Smith bent down and raised it.

On hands and knees Betsie and I crept into the narrow space behind. But once we were in we could stand upright, sit down, or even take turns lying on the single matress. A cunningly masked ventilator in the real wall let in fresh air.

'Take care that there is always a jug of fresh water and a good supply of ship's biscuit,' said Mr Smith. He struck his fist against the wall above the bookcase. 'The Gestapo could search here for a year without finding anything.'

The hunt for Jews worsened steadily. We took six Jews into our house. Twice a week we practised for the real thing. We had an electric alarm system. When one of us pressed the alarm button a slight buzzing sound could be heard in every room. When it was at night the Jews had at once to take off their bedclothes and turn their mattress so that the warmth from their bodies should not betray them.

Quickly and silently they hurried into the hiding-place with their clothes, bedclothes and all their little possessions. The whole thing took five minutes at first but after a few practices they only needed seventy seconds.

And then it came.

I was sick and in bed with a temperature. In my feverish sleep I could hear a buzzing sound which wouldn't go away. It went on and on. Why didn't it stop? There were footsteps running, voices whispering. 'Quick! Quick!' I sat bolt upright. People were running past my bed. As I turned round I could see Thea's heels just disappearing through the sliding door. Meta followed her, then Henk.

But − I hadn't planned any practice for today. Who in the world. . . so it must be. . . it must be. . . it was no practice. Eusi rushed past me white in the face. His pipe rattled in the ashtray he held in his trembling hands. And finally it dawned on me that this was no game but in earnest. One, two, three, four people were already in the secret room; five as Eusi's black shoes and bright red socks disappeared. But Mary − where was Mary? The old woman appeared in the bedroom struggling for breath. I jumped out of bed and half pulled, half shoved her across the room. I drew the board down and hurried back to my bed.

Below I could hear doors slamming and heavy feet on the stairs, but another noise froze my blood, the panting rasping breathing of Mary.

I was just back in bed when the bedroom door was thrown open. 'What's your name?'

Slowly and − as I hoped − sleepily I sat up.

'What?'

'What's your name?'

'Cornelia ten Boom.'

'Ah, you're the one!' It was a big heavy man speaking, with a strangely pale face. He looked at me with renewed interest. 'Now tell me where the Jews are hiding.'

'I don't know what you're talking about.'

He laughed. 'Well now, we'll soon show you.'

He called a man in and said: 'You know what you have

to do, Kapteyn.' Kapteyn seized me by the elbow and pushed me before him down the stairs. Another soldier kept guard in the doorway. Kapteyn shoved me into the shop and ordered me to stand against the wall.

'Where are the Jews?'

'What Jews?'

The man landed me a hefty blow on the face.

'Where are the Jews?'

'I don't know what you're. . .'

Kapteyn struck me again. I staggered against a grand-father clock. Before I recovered myself he struck me yet again. Struck me over and over. The blows were very painful and my head fell back.

'Where are the Jews?'

Another blow.

'Where is the secret room?'

I tasted blood in my mouth. My head went sideways, there was a roaring in my ears. 'Lord Jesus,' I cried, 'help me.' Then I lost consciousness. The first thing I heard was hammer blows and the splitting of wood about us. A group of men trained for the job were looking for the secret room.

After a long time a man appeared in the doorway. 'We've searched the whole house,' he said. 'If there's a secret room here then the devil himself must have built it.' The chief of police looked from Betsie to Father and then at me. 'There is a secret room here,' he said quietly, 'and people hidden in it. Very well. We will have the house watched until they all snuff out and turn into mummies.'

Then Father, Betsie and I were taken to prison. I was held for a month in solitary confinement. One day I got a letter from my sister Nollie. The letter had been opened as usual and could not say much because censored. One thing struck me, namely, that Nollie had written the address slanting up to the right in the direction of the stamp. Usually Nollie always wrote straight. The stamp! Could it be that? Excitedly I soaked the stamp off with a little water. Under it there was indeed something written. I stood under the light to decipher the tiny script. It said: 'All the clothes in your cupboard have been saved.' So all six Jews had got out of the secret room, then. They were saved.

Only much later did I learn how it came about. A

30

policeman from Haarlem, called Rolf, secretly worked with us. During the fourth night after the raid he succeeded in being detailed for guard duty at our house. He knew about the hiding-place and set the Jews free. He found them all in good health even though painfully cramped and hungry and took them to another hiding-place.

Corrie's sister Betsie and her father died from the ill-treatment they received in captivity. Corrie was free again in 1945 at the end of the war and so could tell the whole story.

---

20. What constitutes the perfection of prudence?

Not to forget the purpose of life.

Success. . . and then?

A great Spanish writer, Lope de Vega, lay on his deathbed. His life passed before him like a film. He had had great success and been showered with applause throughout his life. He had inspired people with more than a thousand plays. He had lived only for success – should he not be content at the end of such a successful life?

When his last hour drew near he suddenly saw things in a different light. But the doctor attending him said to him in surprise: 'You can die happy. The world will not forget you. You will go down in history.'

'Doctor,' said the dying man, 'I see it all now. Before God only one with a good heart is great. How gladly would I now give all the praise I have had in my whole life if I could do one more good deed in exchange.'

Courage

We have already seen:
    A good knife is a sharp knife.
    A good person is a just person.

    But it is hard to live uprightly always.
    How is it that we leave the straight path of what is right?
    Because of temptation and coercion. Temptation entices
    us, and coercion drives us from the path.

    Temperance withstands temptation.
    Courage withstands coercion.

21. What is courage?

Courage means: holding fast even when danger threatens.

Flying blind

Somewhere over Texas, 12,000 metres up, the trainee pilot Robert Walding was feeling real exhilaration. Next to him sat his instructor, Group Captain Joseph Garner. He was not doing anything, only keeping an eye on things.

The time was 22.45.

Suddenly the right jet reactor of the plane spat flames. It must have been a cut in the oil supply causing it to overheat.

The captain believed the plane to be lost. At once he gave a crisp command: 'Bale out.' Straight away he raised the glass dome of the cockpit and a fierce wind rushed into the plane which was flying at 700 kilometres an hour.

The young man at once pressed the button to eject but nothing happened. Something was not working. With enormous effort Robert turned his head and what he saw made him stiff with fright. The captain's seat was still there but empty. The Group Captain must have been torn away by the wind.

For Robert there remained only one chance of survival and that was to bale out, and quickly. For the engine was spouting flames like a catherine wheel. He bent down to undo his seatbelt. Then all at once he saw a boot. When he looked behind he could see Captain Joseph Garner lying squeezed into the rear part of the cockpit, unconscious.

Robert did not know what to do now. The plane could explode at any moment.

Suddenly the young pilot took a completely crazy decision. He could not jump! He could not leave his unconscious instructor behind. It was a million to one chance but he would risk it.

Robert seized the joystick and went into a dive. The speed went up to 800-900 kilometres. The temperature in the open cockpit was minus 40. Robert was no longer able to close his eyes. The icy storm glued his eyelids back and his eyes were terribly painful.

The plane neared a speed of 1000 kilometres an hour – and that with an open cockpit! Robert counted the seconds in the dive and when he judged he could not be far from the ground he brought the plane back to the horizontal. He groped for the radio control button and called the landing ground: 'This is trainee pilot Robert Walding. I'm blind. Help me.'

A voice answered: 'You are 1700 metres up. We'll try to bring you down.' The voice bade him reduce his speed to 400 kilometres.

Then Robert heard: 'That's it. You are in a line with the runway.' The voice told him to put on his floodlights so that he could be guided in. He felt for the switch but could not find the right button.

'Go around again, take your time! I will tell you exactly where the button is,' came the voice out of the earphones.

Four minutes later the lights went on and he now came full circle. But just before the plane grounded it dipped. The voice said then without a trace of agitation:'You can choose, son. Either you open the throttle and go round again or you draw the wheels in and make a belly landing.'

Robert answered at once: 'I can do no more. I'm coming down.'

Two minutes later the fire engines were racing towards the plane which had flopped down in a gigantic rain of sparks. The plane was drenched with foam. The rescue team were on the spot at once and pulled the two men out.

Captain Garner woke up ten minutes later in hospital. They had to tell him everything.

Robert Walding needed three days before he could see normally again. He will suffer from weak eyesight for the rest of his life.

22. What are the signs of courage?

Putting a bold face on things and above all holding on to the end.

Out of hell

In the early sixties Nicky Cruz was warden of a home for drug addicts in New York. He tells of Sonny who sought out the home in complete despair.

Heroin addiction is one of the most harrowing experiences imaginable. I got a room ready for Sonny on the third floor of our house. As I knew that it was necessary to keep a continuous watch on him I told my wife I would be staying with Sonny the next three nights. I was firmly decided not to leave his bedside until he had calmed down.

On the first day he was restless, walking ceaselessly up and down the room and talking endlessly. In the evening he began shaking. Then I sat the whole night with him as cold shudders seized him and his teeth chattered. Now and again he would break away from me and run to the door though I had locked it and he could not get out.

At dawn on the second day the shaking lessened somewhat and I took him downstairs for some breakfast. Then I suggested a walk round the block but he had hardly reached the street than he was twisted with pain and had to give in. I straightened him up but he broke free and ran up the road and collapsed. I dragged him back to the pavement and held his hand until the attack was over and he came to himself again. We went back to his room on the third floor.

Towards evening he cried: 'Nicky, I can't do it. I can't do it.'

'No, Sonny, we'll do it together. God will give us the strength.'

'I don't want strength. I want a *fix*. I must have one. Please, please, Nicky. Let me go. For God's sake let me go.'

'No, Sonny, for God's sake I won't let you go. You are very precious to God. I'm keeping you here until you're well again.'

36

He was bathed in sweat and threw up repeatedly so that I feared he would rupture his stomach. I cooled his forehead with damp cloths and helped as much as I could.

By evening he fell into a restless sleep. He groaned and tossed about. Twice he jumped up and tried to get to the door. The second time I had to put him back to bed by force. I had not slept for forty-two hours and could hardly keep my eyes open. But if I fell asleep Sonny would slip away perhaps never to be seen again. We had almost won through but I could fight no more. My chin sank onto my chest and I thought: 'If I could only close my eyes for a few minutes. . .'

With a start I sat upright. A paling light from the street lamps entered the bare room. I thought indeed I had closed my eyes only a few seconds but something told me it must have been a good deal longer. Sonny's bed was empty.

I jumped up and was running to the door when I saw him by the window. A wave of relief swept through me. Snow was falling outside. The road and pavement were merged into a white carpet and the branches and buds of the tree in front of the window sparkled under the white flakes.

Sonny said, 'It's wonderful. It's unbelievable. I've never seen anything so beautiful, Have you?' I stared at him. His eyes were clear and his speech no longer clumsy.

He smiled, 'God is good, Nicky. It's wonderful. Tonight he got me out of hell. I'm free.'

I looked at the lovely scene before us and whispered: 'Thank you, God. Thank you.' Beside me Sonny whispered: 'Thank *you*.'

23. Why does a courageous person need patience rather than heroics?

Because there are more often occasions for bearing with others than for saving them from drowning.

'Take St Vincent water'

Once a woman went to St Vincent Ferrer. She complained bitterly of her husband that he was grumbling and bad-tempered; there was no putting up with him. Vincent Ferrer could perhaps show her a way of bringing back peace to the house.

'Go to our monastery,' said the saint, 'and tell the porter he is to give you some water from the cloister well. Then when your husband comes home you take a sip of the water. But be careful to hold it in your mouth. Then you will see wonders.'

The woman faithfully did what the saint bade her. When her man came home in the evening his ill-humour and impatience soon started. Quickly the woman took some of the miracle water and pressed her lips together so as to be sure to keep it in her mouth.

Really! Her husband soon fell silent! And the storm was quickly over that day.

The woman tried the secret cure several times: always with the same wonderful result. From then on her husband gradually changed. He answered her affectionately and even praised her gentleness and patience.

The woman, rejoicing over her husband's new state of mind, hastened to the saint and beaming with happiness told him the result of the secret remedy.

'It was not the water from the cloister well that I gave you, daughter, that worked the miracle,' the saint said laughing. 'Before, you irritated your husband by answering back: your silence tamed him.'

Now there is a Spanish proverb: 'Take St Vincent water.'

How would it be if now and again we took a sip of that water too?

38

24. What is generosity?

Generosity is sparing nothing to achieve a noble purpose.

Adding a nought

Cardinal Alexander Farnese (later Pope Paul III) was very open-handed.

One day a poor young mother asked him for five silver pieces which she desperately needed.

The cardinal sent his secretary to give the lady fifty silver pieces.

'This is a mistake. I only asked for five silver pieces,' said the woman. But the secretary showed her a note in which the cardinal had in fact written 50.

The good young mother went with the note in her hand to the cardinal. 'Your Eminence,' she cried, 'you've made a mistake with the nought here.'

'Yes indeed, you are right,' answered the cardinal. Then he took his pen and smiling added another nought.

Taken aback the good woman read: 500 silver pieces!

25. What is presumption?

Presumption is a false bravery which thinks it can do the impossible.

A snail to the attack

A snail which lived on a railway embankment got annoyed every day by an express train rushing past and disturbing her at her work.

'I'll cure it of that!' said the snail to herself, took up a position between the rails of the track and stretched her horns out threateningly when she saw the train appearing in the distance. 'I'll derail it,' she threatened.

The train came on and roared over the enemy and sped away. The snail turned round and looked after the speeding train as it retreated. 'It wouldn't stop', she said disgusted, 'it's gone off. The coward!'

---

26. Is someone who has no fear a brave person?

No, one who stays calm and sensible in spite of fear.

'On three I shoot'

Bill Blackwood was once invited by friends to their country house on the Hudson. So one Saturday he set off and found a crowd of guests already at the villa. Needless to say on that particular evening more than lemonade was taken. Towards the end of the evening the host came up to Bill:

'My dear Bill, I shall have to put you in the haunted room. All the others are full up.'

'Oh, a pleasure,' replied Bill.

'Oh, Mr Blackwood,' called out some of the ladies admiringly, 'aren't you bothered about the ghost? Don't you know that poor woman who committed suicide thirty years ago walks there?'

'How do you know, seeing no one has been willing to sleep there? What's remarkable about that? It has a grand view. Good night ladies.'

A quarter of an hour later Bill was lying in his pyjamas on the bed in the haunted room. He had all the same laid his revolver on the bedside table and left the light on in the room.

As he was dropping off to sleep he suddenly noticed five

small black fingers slowly moving at the end of the bed. . .

Bill opened his eyes wide, closed them, opened them again. . .

The five small black fingers were still there. . . and all at once there were ten of them. Bill raised himself slightly.

'Stop your silly game,' he said. 'Show your face or I shoot.'

And cool and calm, he seized his revolver. The little hands moved almost beseechingly but no face came into view.

'I shan't say it again,' called Bill. 'On three I shoot.' And he took careful aim. The little hands stayed stock still. 'Stand up or I shoot,' yelled Bill.

The ten little fingers began to tremble a little. 'One,' called Bill. 'Two. Three.' And he pulled the trigger. Since then Bill has been lame in one foot!

---

27. Why is arrogance so ridiculous?

Because it exaggerates one's worth,

One nil

George Bernard Shaw was once asked by a conceited member of the upper class: 'Is it true, Mr Shaw, that your father was a tailor?'

'Yes, that is so.'

'Then there's something I don't follow,' quipped his lordship. 'How is it that you too did not become a tailor?'

Shaw smiled. He looked the other up and down and asked:

'Tell me, young man, is it true your father was a gentleman?'

'Undoubtedly.'

'Then I don't understand,' retorted Shaw thoughtfully, 'how is it that you are not a gentleman?'

28. Is it courageous to risk one's life merely for show?

No, it is courageous to risk one's life if it is for a good reason.

A reckless dare

One day a group of students in Ohio discovered a new game. A boy and a girl would sit opposite each other on the railway track and wait there until a long-distance express came rushing along. The one who stayed sitting there the longer and let the train come nearest would be the winner.

One such 'railist', as the dangerous game came to be known, brought two young people to within a hair's-breadth of death. When a group of them were on the way home after a dance where they had been drinking, Lilian Ramsay, uncrowned queen of the party for her loveliness and her proud ways, challenged her escort to go on the rails with her. How could he say no and get the name of being less daring than she? So he accepted the challenge and only a few minutes after they had got down on the dangerous track they heard the night express thundering towards them. 'It was obvious to me,' the young man said afterwards, 'that Lilian would rather let herself be crushed to a pulp by the train than give up before I did. To save her I had to be the loser. So I jumped away from the sleepers and grabbed her with me.'

But it was too late. It's true he came out of it with no more than a torn coat but Lilian was grazed by the engine. She paid for her dare with a broken shoulder-blade and a few cracked ribs and in falling her face was so damaged that the stitches from her cuts not only spoiled her beauty but she was marked for life with the scars.

42

29. What does risking one's life in a noble cause mean?

It means to give one's life to save another in some way.

One in a thousand

The engines of the mechanised column were roaring and shuddering up the steep climb. In the clear morning air the mountain landscape was magical.

'Sergeant,' asked the young soldier, 'weren't you afraid the first time you came under fire?'

Sergeant Schiermer had to laugh: 'D'you imagine I'm not afraid today? I'm only human like you. Whenever there's danger I feel afraid. Only you learn in time not to worry about it so much.'

This answer seemed to calm Blondeau who was in action for the first time. 'I thought I was being a coward,' he remarked, 'because I've been frightfully afraid since we started.'

Sergeant Schiermer was known to be one of the best drivers in the French troops in Vietnam. On that 5 June 1948 he was driving fourth in the column consisting of one hundred vehicles in all. His big lorry was jokingly called 'Painless' because at the first hit from the enemy it would go up in the air. It was in fact packed tight with ammunition and explosives. That day the enemy hidden in the jungle had already let pass three golden opportunities of getting at the column. The fourth and last danger spot remained, the highest mountain pass before the descent into the valley. On the right the mountain side rose up covered in forest. On the left of the narrow single track it fell away fifty metres down into a ravine.

The first three armoured cars had already disappeared down into the valley when the first shots came. The enemy fire was aimed at the engine of the fourth vehicle. The intention was obvious: destroy the lorry and block up the narrow road. Then the massacre could begin: the whole column would be shut in behind and delivered over to the hidden enemy.

Schiermer had already realised the purpose of the enemy attack. In no time at all his engine was on fire and a front tyre had burst. The lorry kept swinging off the road to the right. With all his strength Schiermer forced the great steering wheel to the left. Then he shouted to the young companion: 'Jump out sharp.' The young soldier guessed what the sergeant had in mind and cried: 'No, no, not that!' The sergeant was furious: 'Out!' Blondeau opened the door and jumped. He took cover behind a stone wall. With the last of his strength Schiermer hauled on the heavy steering wheel to the left. The lorry disappeared over the edge of the road and plunged down over the precipice. A fearful explosion shook the valley.

Now the pass was free. Blondeau was able to jump into the next vehicle and the whole column accelerated and got away, to the stupefaction of the enemy.

It had been such a powerful explosion that no trace of Sergeant Schiermer was found. Through his courageous decision he saved a thousand of his comrades.

---

30. What is the height of bravery?

To give one's life for one's beliefs.

He followed his conscience

Ivan Moissejew was a soldier in the Red Army. He died in July 1972, through drowning, according to the official report. Every means was employed to prevent his parents from seeing their son before he was buried. But the parents insisted, the coffin was opened. Those standing round were shocked. It was at once clear that the young man had not drowned but had died under blows and grievous ill-treatment.

What had happened?

Ivan's last messages to his parents are particularly revealing. On 14 July 1972 he wrote: 'News from your son will soon be at an end. They have forbidden me to speak of Jesus Christ.'

Another time he informed them: 'They gave me nothing to eat for five days. Then they asked me: "Now, have you changed your mind?" '

In the last letter before his death we read: 'A battle for Christ lies before me and I go to the fight at Jesus' command. I mean to show how a believer should live. Where the way leads for me after that I cannot know.'

But we know: for this young soldier the way led to martyrdom.

Temperance

Temperance is the fourth and last of the cardinal virtues.

If we compare these four most important human virtues with an airplane, justice is the engine, the driving force. But drive alone is not enough. There needs to be a driver: prudence is the pilot. Courage and temperance are the two wings which give lift: without them the plane crashes. Not to be both courageous and controlled is to risk failing in integrity.

31. Why do we admire self-control?

**Because it means to remain master
of our immoderate and destructive urges.**

The accident

It was at the end of July 1984, on a Friday night. The atmosphere in the disco was great. Still Bridget said at 1.30: 'I must go home now. Who's driving us back?' The reason was her brother's wedding that Saturday.

It was Gerard, rather far gone in drink, who offered to drive Bridget and her friend Gaby home. They hadn't far to go. From Topmeadow to Underwood is only five miles. The nineteen-year-old Gerard was glad of the chance to show the girls what he could do. He raced down the dangerous Topmeadow Hill at 90 miles an hour. On the first bend he went into a skid on the wet road and lost control of the vehicle. The car went off the road, crashed into a tree and landed in the middle of bushes. After about an hour Gaby managed to get the back door open and crawl out. She ran in the direction of Underwood until a car picked her up. The girl was in such a state of shock that the driver had to inform the police.

When the police learned that there were still two persons trapped in the car they called in the fire brigade to help. The firemen set to work at once to free the two hapless young people. After some difficulty they succeeded in forcing an opening in the twisted metal.

Gerard soon recovered from his injuries. Gaby had to spend five months in hospital. For Bridget help had come to late. She died, only 17, on the way to hospital.

32. Why does self-restraint liberate us?

Because it stops us from being ruled by the desire for pleasure.

Hans and Helga

Hans, only son of a business man, grew up in a small town. For almost a year he had been close friends with Rosemarie, daughter of a radio mechanic in the town. The two young people thought they were really in love and when Hans had a promotion they decided to get engaged.

Hans' mother, who adored her only son, was against this early engagement. But Hans got his way with his mother over this as with everything else he wanted.

Shortly after, Hans was called up for military service and sent to a station 750 km away.

During the first weeks and months Hans was fully occupied settling in to a new life. Rosemarie's letters came regularly, they were his only joy, and he eagerly wrote back. They saw each other again at Christmas and this time the parting was even harder.

But to his surprise Hans found that the barracks had meanwhile become almost a second home to him. It was good to see his pals again, they all had so much to tell – their successes with girls included, of course. Hans was impressed as he listened to the exploits of the others. A natural reserve stopped him from saying anything about Rosemarie, and his pals teased him for holding back. To prove to them he was man he went the next free evening to the local dance hall where soldiers and girls met. He drank a little, danced a lot – why not? – and afterwards had the feeling that there were other pretty girls around besides Rosemarie.

One of the girls he made acquaintance with on the dance floor was sixteen-year-old Helga who had fallen head over heels in love with the young soldier. It followed naturally that Hans took up with her more and more and that made Helga happy. She had no suspicion that Hans was engaged; she believed he loved her – although he had never used the word to her. For the inexperienced Helga his caresses and kisses were proof enough.

Rosemarie's letters brought no joy to Hans now, they only pricked his conscience. But he told himself that what he was doing was a young man's right — the behaviour and talk of his comrades confirmed him in this way of looking at it.

He was moody, overbearing and intolerant with Helga and she loved him all the more for it. But when he wanted her to give herself to him she held back. Hans stood her up.

Helga did not suspect that for Hans this occasion for a break between them had been welcome. She was deadly miserable, did not know how to go on, could not imagine life without Hans.

But Hans that night wrote a really genuine love letter to his betrothed for the first time in a long while; a weight had gone from his heart because he had at last put an end to the unhappy situation.

It was only weeks later that he let himself be persuaded by his pals to go with them to the dance hall. Helga, who now was ready to do anything, tried to make it up with him. But he told her brutally that he had never loved her and she could go to the devil.

Helga however believed that she had only lost him because she hadn't readily given herself to him. She did it very easily for a friend of his who had been observing how things were developing. She simply could not understand when he also left her. Finally she was convinced that men are like that, forced herself not to take love seriously any longer, became a light woman the soldiers in the barracks passed from hand to hand.

David Wilkerson has a word to say on the subject: 'Sex is something so great that God put it into the care of marriage. Outside of marriage sex is wrong. It's as simple as that. In this way God protects family, home and country. No tender feelings of love can change this any more than a leap off the Eiffel Tower alters the force of gravity.'

33. What has temperance to say about eating?

We should eat to live and not the reverse.

On a water diet

The millionaire Baron Rothschild was once consulting the 'water doctor' Father Kneipp. Rothschild sank into the armchair and began in complaining tones: 'I feel so bad, Father. Even in the morning I wake up with a headache, by midday I'm feeling dizzy, after a meal I'm so exhausted.'

'Tell me,' interrupted Kneipp. 'What did you have for lunch today?

'Lunch today? Oh, nothing special. First ravioli for *hors d'oeuvre*, then soup, viennese steak with pineapple, roast venison with red wine sauce. But tell me, Father, what's the matter with me?'

'I can tell you right away. What you need is a second stomach!'

34. Why must the very first step towards a bad habit be avoided?

Because there's no more stopping it than a landslide.

Once doesn't count

There are said to be six million alcoholics in France. Hear how one of these alcoholics, the singing priest Lucien Duval, now dead, describes the hell of alcoholism.

Alcohol was more than a physical urge. It was also psychological. For two months after my first drying out I stayed off alcohol. Then I was invited to my nephew's wedding. There was dancing at the reception. Everyone was happy and relaxed. My nephew came up to me and said: 'Uncle, will you drink a glass of champagne with us?'

In my head a small voice said: 'One glass, only one glass. One doesn't count. I must join in with the rest,' I told myself, 'I can't cut myself off.' There was an inner conflict lasting only a couple of seconds and I said: 'Gladly.'

Next day I drank two glasses of red wine in the afternoon and four in the evening.

And everything started inexorably all over again: the despair, the self-disgust, the shame. It was as though I was on a treadmill.

I loathed myself. I no longer had the excuse of ignorance. I knew I wasn't able to stop. The freedom to keep off alcohol was gone. The end could only be death.

Duval had given up all human hope. But he still hoped in Christ. And that hope was not in vain. He again became free of alcohol.

---

35. Why do we use different measures for ourselves and for others?

Because our self-love comes first and finds excuses for ourselves.

It's the other's fault

Once a peasant woman was going to the market. She wanted to exchange her butter for rice.

She soon found a buyer and all went well. But after about an hour she came back very annoyed to the man who sold her the rice.

'Just you listen, you! Your kilo of rice is fifty grams short.'

'How can that be,' said the astonished dealer, 'I weighed the rice against the kilo of butter you brought.'

36. What should we examine our consciences about specially?

About restraint in speech: have I said anything behind people's backs?

Three sieves

One day a man came to Socrates, very upset.
'Hey, Socrates, have you heard what your friend has done? Just let me tell you.'
'One moment,' interrupted the sage. 'Have you put what you are going to tell me through three sieves?'
'Three sieves?' asked the other in amazement.
'Yes my dear fellow, three sieves. Let's see whether what you have to tell me will go through three sieves. The first sieve is truth. Have you proof of everything you want to tell me?'
'No, I heard it said and. . .'
'Quite so. But you have certainly tested it with the second sieve. It is the sieve of goodness. What you want to tell me – if it can't be shown to be true – is it at least something good?'
Hesitatingly the other said: 'No, it's not; the opposite. . .'
'Aha!' broke in Socrates. 'So let's also make use of the third sieve and ask ourselves whether it is necessary to tell me what you are so excited about.'
'Not strictly necessary. . .'
'Well then,' said the wise man smiling, 'if what you want to tell me is neither true, nor good, nor necessary, then bury it and don't burden yourself with it.'

37. Why is a pure atmosphere important for the whole of a person?

Because pollution harms the body and pornography the mind.

The pudding

Nicky Cruz the one-time New York gangster tells this story;

A family was having difficulties with their ten-year-old daughter Mary Ann because she wanted to see a particular film.

'Everybody's going except me,' she wailed to her mother. 'Why can't I?'

The mother was just mixing a pudding. 'Mary Ann,' was all she said, 'where are the bad eggs I found this morning on the top shelf?'

'They're in the bin. Why?'

'Bring them here, please.'

'What are you going to do with them?'

'Put them into the pudding.'

'Bad eggs! They'll spoil a lovely pudding.'

'Ah,' was the mother's rejoinder, 'if the pudding is spoiled I can always throw it away. But if you stuff your head with that kind of filth − and that's what this film is − I can't just throw you away.'

Nicky Cruz adds:

We must face the facts: pornographic magazines, films and shows today constitute one of the most lucrative businesses in the world.

38. Why is integrity so important in the
nation's leaders?

**Because they receive attractive offers
and 'the chance is all that matters. . .'**

The Tiger

The French Premier, Georges Clemenceau was very strict
and conscientious. For this reason he was called The Tiger.

One day he was asked by an impertinent reporter: 'Why
do ordinary people not like you?'

Back came the answer: 'Because I tell them the truth. The
times are bad. People must be content with less.'

'Why are you not liked by important people and politicians either?'

'Because I am not corrupt. I take no money from people
seeking a good post.'

'So are you the only upright politician in France?'

'No, no. They are all upright — as long as they don't come
under temptation.'

39. Why should we sometimes laugh at
ourselves and our achievements?

**Because we are none of us as
important as we like to think.**

Half dead

Doctor Thulesius of Bremen had a sense of humour. An
anxious patient once asked him: 'Doctor, is it still possible
today to be buried without being really dead?'

'Absolutely not,' replied Dr Thulesius firmly. 'Anyone
who gets into the hands of a doctor nowadays is dead.'

40. Why is pride so dangerous?

Because it refuses to see the reality.

Pride comes before a fall

A. J. Cronin has a tale from his life as a young doctor in Scotland:

At the beginning of May scarlet fever broke out in the village area and in a bad way. It was especially the children in the village who fell ill and the epidemic refused to respond to the usual measures. As the days went by and case followed case in spite of all our efforts I lost patience and told myself I had to get to the root of the matter. There must decidedly be some special cause for the spread of the disease and I would find it.

All the cases I handled had one thing in common and that was that they had their milk from Farmer Shawhead. I had of course no proof, only a surmise; but that was sufficient to spur me on. As I was passing Shawhead's the following Tuesday morning I called in at the farm.

It was a pretty farm with climbing roses already coming into flower over the whitewashed buildings. As far as the eye could see everything was neat and clean, the farmhouse all in order, the outbuildings looked in good repair and the surrounding fields well tended. No wonder that Shawhead was proud of it. He was a rough stocky man of about fifty. His whole life was centred on two great interests: his property which he had inherited from his forebears and his young wife Jean whom he had lately married and, in spite of his roughness, simply adored.

When I knocked at the bright green door Jean herself opened it and at my question shook her head smiling.

'No,' she answered, 'my husband is not in. He's taken a couple of calves to market. He won't be back all this afternoon.'

She really was a pretty young woman. Not more than twenty-three, she had innocence about her and with it a certain liveliness.

56

'So Shawhead is not here,' I remarked to gain time.
'No,' she replied, 'but he'll be back around four. Will you come in or can I offer you something?'
I hesitated. 'You see, Mrs Shawhead, I've come about a rather special matter. This scarlet fever epidemic. . . it's spreading, you understand; and I have found that all my patients. . . well, to cut it short, in every case they have their milk from Shawhead. I want to be quite open with you. I want to ask whether I might look round. . . to see whether there is a cause for it here.'
Although I had spoken in friendly fashion her manner changed. Her face darkened and she tossed her head. 'The scarlet fever,' she cried indignantly, 'fancy mentioning that in the same breath with our good milk! Really, Doctor, if that's why you've come you would do better to speak to my husband.' And without another word she slammed the door in my face.
That same afternoon I again drove to Shawhead's farm and knocked once more on the bright green door. But there was no answer. So I went past the farmhouse to the barn to look for Shawhead.
When I reached the cowsheds the farmhand was just driving the cows in for milking. I leant against the door and watched as the handsome shining beasts took up their places in the stalls. Then I watched the farmhand, David, take up the three-legged stool, and sit down by the first cow, his cheek against her swelling flank, and begin milking.
My eyes rested as though mesmerised on David, for David looked sick and pale and he had a rag of red flannel round his neck.
Quietly I went forward and greeted David.
'It's you, Doctor,' he said, 'I had no idea you were here. Will you have a glass of milk?'
Unsmiling I shook my head. 'I don't want milk today David.' Then I pointed casually to the red flannel. 'What's the matter with your throat?' David stopped milking and laughed awkwardly. 'Oh it's nothing, nothing at all. I had a sore throat a week or so ago and since then I've been a bit off colour. But it's nothing – nothing at all.'
My gaze moved yet closer. 'Sore throat,' I repeated.
Then all at once I saw David's hands and was shocked.

57

I had no need to look further. The answer was in David's hands so busily milking the cow, for on both hands the skin was peeling. Then I was sure the milk was contaminated.

Suddenly a loud voice broke the quiet of the cowshed.

'So you're here too? Spying and meddling in other people's affairs.'

Shawhead appeared in person, red with rage. Behind him stood his wife looking at me reproachfully. It was a painful moment. However, I could not now avoid an explanation.

'Forgive me, Shawhead, I'm not here on my own account but out of real necessity.' I pointed to the farmhand. 'David has had scarlet fever, apparently only a slight attack but enough to cause great harm.' I measured my words as best I could. 'It seems you will have to close youre dairy for one or two weeks.'

'What?' cried Shawhead half in amazement, half in fury. 'Close the dairy? You're not right in the head.'

'Do be reasonable,' I begged, 'there's no blame attached to you. But the fact remains that the infection is coming from here.'

'The infection? How dare you, man! Everything here is perfectly clean.'

'Yes but David. . .'

'David is as clean as the rest,' cried Shawhead. 'He's had a bit of a sore throat, that's all. Now he's better. Better, d'you hear? It's complete madness to suggest we have to close on that account.'

'I tell you,' I insisted with all the patience I could muster, 'he has had scarlet fever. He's peeling all over. That is contaminating your milk.'

The veins in Shawhead's temples stood out. He could not contain himself. 'That's enough! I want not another word from you. The very idea! My beautiful milk contaminated! It's good pure milk and always has been. Don't you know we drink it ourselves?' In great indignation he seized the dipper and plunged it in the milk. Defiantly he raised the frothing can, drank half and then gave the rest to Jean. 'There!' He threw down the empty can. 'That'll show you. And if you say one word more you'll regret it.'

I paused a moment. I understood the farmer's wounded pride. But I had my duty to do. I went in silence.

I asked the Health Service to check on the matter. But the doctor in charge was in no hurry. He wanted no difficulties with the wealthy Shawhead.

A few days later I was sitting dejectedly in my consulting room when my colleague Dr Cameron came in with a strange expression on his face.

'Have you heard yet?' He spoke in a low constrained voice. 'It's got her. Acute scarlet fever. Shawhead's wife Jean herself.'

Momentary astonishment. Like lightning I remembered the defiant action with which Shawhead passed on the milk can to Jean.

'It would seem Shawhead is quite beside himself with worry and anxiety', Dr Cameron was saying.

Soon word went round that Jean Shawhead was severely ill. Her temperature rose rapidly and she lay in delirium. On the Sunday it was said she was dying. Towards evening Janet, our housekeeper, came into the living room. Her voice was sombre as she said: 'It's all over now. She's dead.'

Six weeks later I came across Shawhead for the first time since our meeting in the cowshed. The farmer, aged and broken by his loss, was returning from the cemetery on the hillside behind the village church. Embarrassed I stood still in the middle of the road and Shawhead too remained standing there almost mechanically. Our eyes met and each read in the other's eyes the knowledge of what might have been, the fearful realisation that his wife could now have been alive and bright at his side, not in her cold narrow grave.

A groan burst from Shawhead's pale lips. Slowly he stretched out his hand to take mine in a slow and painful grip.

BEING CHRISTIAN

When I was eighteen

At eighteen I was doing my military service. I was posted to Paris. For the first time in my life I was living with people of no belief. Of the thirty soldiers in our section I was the only one to go to church on a Sunday.

In that situation I began doubting. My comrades were basically sincere and friendly. And yet they had no thought for God or religion. So it was possible to get along without faith. And besides why should I alone be in the right and all the others in error?

So I gradually became unbelieving at heart. Within me there was darkness. But God gave me a light in my night. I had an aunt I was very fond of, Aunt Teresa. She was a nurse and goodness itself. She had never married and had been all her life a quiet helper in all kinds of spiritual and material needs for innumerable people.

I took the opportunity of a furlough to go and visit Aunt Teresa. She lived in a small town near Paris.

In the afternoon I went out for a walk alone and sat for a while on the parapet of a bridge over a beautiful river. An old tramp came past and stopped for a rest. We got into conversation. All at once he pointed to my aunt's house: 'You see that little place over there?' he said with emotion, 'the best woman in these parts lives there. She's hardly anything herself and yet she does everything she can to help our sort.'

In that instant it became clear to me: my aunt is by far the best person I know — and she is a committed Christian. Mustn't a faith which is such a power for love be true? And that was how I found my way back to the faith.

The Apostles' Creed

I believe in God, the Father almighty,
   creator of heaven and earth.

I believe in Jesus Christ, his only Son, our Lord.
   He was conceived by the power of the Holy Spirit
      and born of the Virgin Mary.
   He suffered under Pontius Pilate,
      was crucified, died, and was buried.
   He descended to the dead.
   On the third day he rose again.
   He ascended into heaven,
      and is seated at the right hand of the Father.
   He will come again to judge the living and the dead.

I believe in the Holy Spirit,
   the holy catholic Church,
   the communion of saints,
   the forgiveness of sins,
   the resurrection of the body,
   and the life everlasting. Amen.

41. What does the Bible say about the
mystery of God?

**God is love: Father, Son and Holy
Spirit are one.**

Why does God allow it?

Max Ellerbusch, a young American engineer, gives the
following autobiographical account:

It was one hectic Friday, six days before Christmas 1958.
I was in my electrical workshop and working feverishly so
as to have a holiday free to be with my family. Suddenly
the telephone rang and a voice at the other end informed
me that our five-year-old Craig had been run over by a car.
I dropped everything and rushed to the spot.

Around him stood a crowd of people but as I approached
they drew back. Craig lay in the middle of the road, his fair
curls with not a hair out of place.

That same afternoon he died in the children's hospital.

It happened at the crossing by the school. A car had come
up so quickly that no one saw it. One boy had shouted, made
a sign, and had to leap out of the way to save his own life.
The vehicle had not even slowed down.

My wife Grace and I drove home from the hospital
through the streets decorated for Christmas. We just could
not grasp what had happened. It wasn't until the evening
when I went past his empty bed that the reality entered my
consciousness. Suddenly tears came not only because of the
empty bed but above all on account of the emptiness and
futility of life which I felt.

Of our four children it was especially Craig who helped
us most to cope with the cares of life. As a baby he smiled
so joyously on the world that people often stopped by his
baby-carriage. When we were visiting, it was three-year-old
Craig who would be the one to say: 'You have a lovely
home.' When he was given a present he was moved to tears
and he would give it to the next child he met that wanted it.

If such a child has to die — I thought as I lay in bed and

tossed from side to side during the night of that fatal Friday
— if such a life can be snuffed out in one minute then life
has no meaning and faith in God is self-deception. In the
morning my state of helplessness had found an outlet: a blind
hatred awoke in me of the man who had done this to us.
The police had meanwhile arrested him in Tennessee. George
Williams he was called, and he was aged fifteen.

The police learned that he came from a broken home.
His mother had taken on night work and slept during the
day. That Friday he had absconded from school, taken her
keys as she slept and driven at top speed down the road.
All my anger at this turn of fate seemed concentrated on
the name George Williams. I called our solicitor and asked
him to prefer the severest charges. 'Try to arrange for him
to be dealt with as an adult. The juvenile courts are not strict
enough.'

Such was my state of mind when something happened that
changed my life entirely. I cannot explain, only describe.

Late on Saturday night I was pacing up and down in the
room next to our bedroom, my fists pressed to my temples.
I felt ill and dizzy and tired — so fearfully tired. 'O God,'
I prayed, 'show me why this had to happen.'

And in that very instant, between one step and the next,
my life was changed. By the inner light of that moment the
realisation suddenly dawned on me that this life has only
one single purpose. It is like a school year and we have just
one subject: love.

'O Craig,' I thought out loud, 'little Craig, in your five
short years you have learnt a lot. What rapid progress you
made, how soon you were ready to move up to a higher
class.'

Grace was sitting up in bed when I opened the bedroom
door. She wasn't reading, wasn't doing anything. She simply
stared in front of her as she had done almost the whole time
since Friday.

I took her hand and tried to tell her that the world is not
ruled by blind fate, that life has meaning, that suffering on
this earth is not the end but leading to a happiness far beyond
our wildest hopes.

'This evening,' I said to her, 'Craig doesn't need us any
more. But somebody needs us. George Williams. And it's

Christmas. Perhaps there's no Christmas present for him in detention unless we send him one.'

Grace listened and stared at me silent and unmoved. Suddenly she burst into tears. 'Yes,' she said, 'that's right. It's the first thing that has been right since Craig's death.'

And that is how it was. George turned out to be an intelligent, lost and lonely boy who needed a father just as much as I needed a son. He had his Christmas present and his mother received a box of Grace's good Christmas fare. We applied for his release and managed it too a few days later, and our house became his second home.

After school now he works with me in the workshop, joins us for meals round the kitchen table and is elder brother to Diana, Michaela and Ruth Carol.

---

42. Who is Jesus?

He is God's Son who became man for us.

One of us

It was 1950. The old Cardinal of Naples did not know what to think. He had already seen a thing or two, but this! A young priest was sitting before him in his office. He was asking permission to be allowed to become a drop-out. He wanted to live on the streets of Naples with the alley-boys.

The old man could not take it in. He knew what the position was in Naples: 200,000 out of work. And all the young boys were hanging round the streets because their parents were without work and could not feed them. They lived by stealing, peddling stolen goods, black marketeering, and begging. They slept in some corner or other. They were like wild cats and dodged the police. This young priest, Mario Borelli, wanted to help them, give them a roof over their heads, bread, and a bit of human warmth.

That the cardinal could understand. But why must the priest become a drop-out himself?

Mario knew exactly why: 'If I go to these boys as a priest they will spit in my face. They are fearfully distrustful.'

The cardinal considered. 'Give me ten days to think it over.'

After ten days the plan was approved.

Mario went on the streets, an old cap back to front on his head, in ragged clothes, a cigarette end in the corner of his mouth. He begged, collected cigarette butts and became a vagrant.

Gradually he won the hearts of these youngsters. Soon he was even the leader of a gang. When he found a primitive shelter his youths went with him. They weren't able to do otherwise — they were drawn to him. This Mario had something irresistible about him. They had no word for it because it was something they had never before experienced. How could they know that the word was love?

Perhaps we can now better understand why God became man. He wanted to be one of us to save us. 'God with us': that is Jesus.

---

43. Why did Jesus die on the cross?

Jesus died on the cross to atone for our sins.

Love even to death

Auschwitz 1941

A prisoner had escaped from the concentration camp.

In the evening camp commandant Fritsch stood before the prisoners. 'The fugitive has not been found,' he roared. 'Ten of you will die in his place in the starvation bunker.' He stepped up to the first row and looked sharply in the face of each one. Finally he raised a hand and pointed: 'That one.'

Pale as a sheet the man stepped forward.

'You — and you — and you. . .'

Ten of them. Condemned to death. One wailed: 'Oh my poor wife and children.'

Suddenly something unexpected happened. A prisoner stepped from the ranks and stood before Fritsch. The commandant grasped his revolver. 'Halt! What does this Polish swine want?' The prisoner answered quietly: 'I would like to die in place of this man.'

'Who are you?'

A brief reply: 'A catholic priest.'

A moment's silence followed. Finally Fritsch made his decision and said gruffly: 'Agreed. Go with the others.'

So died the Franciscan Maximilian Kolbe at only 47. A man who wanted to conquer the world through love. But he knew: 'Greater love has no man than this, that a man lay down his life for his friends' (John 15:13).

---

44. Did Jesus rise from the dead?

Yes he rose again and we too rise with him.

The four-legged theologian

The sick man seized the doctor's hand. 'I'm so afraid to die. Do tell me, doctor, what is waiting for me when I die? What will it be like on the other side?'

'I don't know,' answered the doctor.

'You don't know?' whispered the dying man.

Without further reply the doctor opened the door into the corridor. A dog sprang in, jumped up to him and showed in every way his joy at seeing his master again.

Then the doctor turned back to the sick man and said: 'Did you see how the dog behaved? He has never been in this room before and does not know the people here. But he knew his master was on the other side of the door and so he leaped joyously in as soon as the door opened. Now look: I don't know anything exactly about what is waiting for us after death either, but it is enough for me to know that my master and Lord is on the other side. So when the door opens one day I shall go in with great joy.'

---

45. Why should we specifically honour Mary?

Because being the Mother of Jesus she is also the Mother of God.

Pray for us sinners

This passage comes from the diary of a U-boat sailor in the Second World War:

The day began quietly. The sea was calm. Nothing to be seen of the enemy. Suddenly the alarm bell shrilled. The commander at once gave the order to dive. 'Enemy in sight.'

Shortly afterwards the first torpedoes dropped. We were sitting in the crewroom in readiness. With grim pale faces we waited for the first hit. Each one knew that would be the last.

We heard the roar of the depth charges. The boat sped down through the water.

All at once Hein, opposite me, drew out a rosary from his pocket. He started to pray. That was the first time any of us had prayed in front of the others. . . but no one laughed.

'Hein, give me a bit. I'm a catholic.'

It looked odd; a calloused hand reaching out for a piece of rosary.

Hein pulled off a decade and gave it to the other man.

The fight was raging up above.

'Give me a bit too.'

'Me too.'

Now Hein held only one decade and the cross in his hand.

Five men praying. . . and no one laughed at them.
'Give me the cross. I'm protestant.'
Hein handed over the cross.
For some minutes we forgot the battle raging. After rather
more than an hour we got away.

---

46. What is the Church?

**The Church is the community of
those who believe in Christ.**

Believe in Jesus

Racked for Christ is the title of the book by Richard
Würmbrand. He comes from Romania.

He tells how in 1948 he was taken by the communists.
They shut him up because he declared his faith in Christ
before all the world.

A short time afterwards his wife also was arrested.
Michael, their nine-year-old son, was left alone. The boy
had to struggle hard to live. He grew so embittered that he
lost his faith in Christ. After two years he was allowed a
short visit to his mother. He came into the prison and saw
his mother behind the bars. Police officials stood by. They
had strictly forbidden the mother to speak about religion.

The son scarcely recognised his mother. She was so
changed by the ill-treatment in prison.

Her first words were: 'Michael, believe in Jesus.' In wild
rage the guards tore her away and led her off.

Michael wept as he saw how his mother was dragged off
before he could say a single word to her. But he never forgot
what his mother had told him:'Michael, believe in Jesus.'
And he found his way back to Christ.

There are more than nine hundred million Christians the
world over. They believe in Jesus Christ and have received
life through baptism.

Unhappily the Christians are split into different confessions: so there are Anglicans and Catholics, Orthodox and Evangelical Christians.

Let us often pray: 'Lord Jesus, give us your Spirit so that we may all be one.'

---

47. Who is the visible head of the Catholic Church on earth?

It is the Pope, Bishop of Rome and successor of the Apostle Peter.

The Pope and the Mother Superior

Sister Portess' heart nearly stopped. Before the door stood the Pope himself waiting patiently after a gentle ring at the bell. Pope John XXIII was there to visit a sick priest in the Holy Ghost Hospital in Rome.

The sister pressed the button to let him in and ran off to inform her Mother Superior who came in great excitement. There had never been such an exalted visitor to Holy Ghost Hospital before. She wanted to introduce herself at once and said: 'I am the Mother Superior of the Holy Ghost.'

The Pope smiled benignly and replied: 'I've not got as far as that. I'm only the representative of Jesus Christ.'

48. What happens after death?
The good go to heaven.

Hanged twice

Roger Warren, a weaver from Lancaster in the sixteenth century, was condemned to the gallows because he had aided catholic priests and given them shelter.

The rope was placed round his neck but when the ladder was withdrawn the rope broke and Warren fell to the ground.

After a few moments he recovered consciousness. He knelt and prayed silently, his eyes gazing heavenwards and his face radiant with joy.

The officer in charge of the execution again offered him his liberty if he would deny his faith. Warren rose and said: 'I am as before ever ready to die for Jesus Christ. Do with me what you will.' And he prepared to mount the ladder again.

'Why, what is this?' cried the officer. 'Why all this haste?'

To which Warren replied: 'Had you seen what I have just seen you too would be as eager to die as I.'

The hangman put a stronger rope on him and drew away the ladder. So died the martyr Roger Warren.

49. What happens to the wicked who refuse to repent?

They go into the everlasting pains of hell.

No return

Two fish, searching for food, saw before them a tasty worm. Then said one fish to the other:

'You see that worm? It is stuck on a hook. The hook is fastened to a line. The line hangs from a rod. The rod is in a man's hand. If either of us swallows the worm, then the iron hook bores into his mouth, the man pulls him out and the poor fish ends in the frying-pan.'

Then the other fish said: 'Ha, ha! My grandma used to tell me that tale when I was little. I don't believe such fairy stories. How can anyone know anything about it? There's never been anyone come back from the frying-pan to tell us about it. If you won't eat this delicious worm, I'll finish it off.' And so he did and indeed ended in the frying-pan.

And he did not in fact come back to tell the tale.

Many people say: 'We know nothing about hell: no one has ever come back from there to tell us about it.'

True enough. But Jesus has warned about the everlasting fire. We ought not to take it lightly but try to live according to his word.

50. Who will stand firm at the Last Judgement?

One who has lovingly stood by those in need.

The king and the peasant

This anecdote comes from the early Kingdom of Spain.

One day King Richard went hunting. When deep in the forest he was overtaken by a thunderstorm and found himself suddenly all alone. As it was evening he tried to find his way back to the royal palace but could not. All through the cold night he was out in the open. Tormented with hunger, he wandered endlessly round in the forest.

Wet and exhausted he at last came in the early morning, upon a lonely farmhouse. He knocked at the door, he knocked several times, but no one answered. In despair the king tried the door. It was not fastened and creaked open.

The peasant farmer leapt up from the kitchen table and shouted: 'You scoundrel, you're trying to steal something here. See that you get out or I'll set the dogs on you.'

The king begged and pleaded but the peasant only grew the more angry. Finally he struck the king in the face and slammed the door after him. However the king reached home thanks to some people who were passing by.

Three days later he had the peasant called to the palace. The peasant thought: 'Why am I to go to the king? I've done nothing to him. I don't even know him.'

He had to enter the great hall all by himself and stand before the assembled princes of the kingdom. The king was in his royal robes, the sceptre in his righ hand, on his head the crown.

For a long time he gazed at the trembling peasant in silence. Then he spoke: 'Do you know me?'

The peasant was so struck by these words that thereupon he died.

We too will hear these words at the Last Judgement:

'Do you know me? I was hungry. . . I was sick. . . I was a stranger. . .'

Let us so live that Christ will not have to say to any of us: 'Away with you into everlasting fire! What you did to the least of my brothers you did to me.'

Our Father

Our Father who art in heaven,
hallowed be thy name;
Thy kingdom come;
Thy will be done on earth as it is in heaven.
Give us this day our daily bread;
and forgive us our trespasses
as we forgive those who trespass against us;
and lead us not into temptation,
but deliver us from evil.

51. Why did Jesus teach us such a short prayer?

Because he knew how easily we are distracted at prayer.

Neither horse nor saddle

On this point there is a true story from St Francis de Sales. Francis de Sales was a very good bishop. He lived some 400 years ago.

One day he was riding through a village. There he met a peasant. The peasant said: 'Good morning, Lord Bishop. I must tell you something. Do you know that I can pray without thinking of anything else at all?'

'That is wonderful,' answered the bishop. 'I have never met anyone who could do that. So I should like to give you a reward. Listen. If you can say a whole "Our Father" without thinking of anything else I will give you my fine horse.'

The peasant was very glad at this and began the prayer straight away.

'Our Father who art in heaven, hallowed be thy name. Thy kingdom come. Thy will be done. . . Do I get the saddle as well as the horse?' he asked suddenly.

Then the bishop had to laugh. 'Alas, alas, neither horse nor saddle.'

The peasant saw that he had lost all. He could not even say this quite short prayer without a distraction.

---

52. Why may we say 'Our Father'
to God?

**Because he created us and has
adopted us as his children.**

In the Palace of Versailles

King Louis XV of France had a daughter who was very
haughty.

One day the princess could not find her gold chain. For
no reason she accused her lady-in-waiting.

'Madam,' said the latter in self-defence, 'you do me great
wrong.' Then the princess cried out incensed: 'How dare
you! Do you not know I am a king's daughter?'

The lady-in-waiting answered calmly: 'And I am a child
of *God*.'

---

53. Why do we say 'in heaven'?

**Because we put our trust in
God's power.**

Is there anybody listening?

The drills pounded crunching into stone, the chisel and pick
hammered with measured thud. Everything was as usual in
the French mine. In a fairly distant gallery deep down six
miners panted and sweated at their toil.

They had hardly resumed drill and chisel after the
breakfast break when Farel lowered his tool.

'I don't know,' he muttered, 'but the air seems a bit queer.
Do you smell anything?'

'I don't like it either,' nodded the foreman, 'perhaps we
should. . .' Before he reached the end of the sentence a fearful

crashing and splitting shook the mine. Then everything went dark and quiet. Only the light of a couple of miners' lamps struggled through the darkness.

'We're trapped,' stammered Farel, his lips trembling.

'We're all done for,' groaned Pierre, 'The whole mountain has caved in.'

'Nonsense! They'll fetch us out,' countered Marcel. 'They'll have to get us! I want to live!'

'Yes, they couldn't just leave us stuck down here like animals,' sobbed Farel. 'I've a wife and three children.'

'It can be several days before they get to us,' shrugged the foreman, and added softly: 'If they manage it at all.'

'Hey you!' Pierre sprang to his feet. 'What did you say? If they manage at all. Is that what you said?'

'Quieten down, Pierre! You won't make things any better by shouting.'

'What is to become of us then?' asked Marcel.

'If they don't rescue us we shall starve to death.'

'Just how long can a man last without food?'

'A week,' cried one.

'Ten or twelve days,' another thought.

'Let's shout, tap out signals,' suggested Farel. 'Perhaps the rescue team is already near.'

'No sense in that. No one will hear us down here,' answered the foreman. 'First we have to hear they're there, then there's some point in giving signals.'

Time dragged by endlessly. Nobody knew whether they had passed minutes or hours in that fearsome tomb. The lamps began to flicker. One after the other they went out. Not a gleam of light pierced the horrid blackness.

Suddenly Pierre began raving, screaming aloud and beating his fists against the black walls. It was some time before they could overpower him and the young man sank down with a groan.

So time dragged on. Hunger and thirst began to torment them. Flasks and lunchboxes were empty. And again the driving thoughts! Will they find us in fact? How long will it be before they stumble on our gallery? If only we could hear something going on!

'Doesn't anyone hear us, no one at all?' wailed Marcel. 'There must be somebody listening.'

82

'If we could only believe there was a God. . .' suggested Farel hesitantly. 'If we only knew that.'

'And what then?' put in Pierre.

'Then we could pray and he would hear us.'

'And? And then?'

'Then he could rescue us.'

'But there is no God. That's only priests' tales,' murmured Marcel dully.

'D'you think so?' Farel asked slowly.

'Well, perhaps it's not a story at all, that about the good God, and if he does exist then he must hear us,' said the foreman almost to himself.

'And perhaps he will save us,' stammered Pierre, 'We ought to try and say a prayer.'

'Who knows how to pray?' asked the foreman.

'I knew a prayer once,' said Farel, 'but now I only know the first two words: Our Father.'

'Our Father,' nodded the others. 'If we only knew how it goes on. Let's try and remember.'

Finally after much thinking the miners had put the whole text together. Over and over again now they prayed the 'Our Father' each one softly to himself, then again all together, devoutly as in church, beseeching, weeping, moaning, always repeating the same form of words: 'Our Father who art in heaven. . .' Hunger and thirst tortured them in their dungeon. Now and again one or another would cry out in despair. But then the great prayer could be heard again spoken by someone else: 'Our Father. . .'

No one could say how long the miners had been entombed when the digger Farel started up out of a dull half sleep. Was that a trick of his feverish senses or had he really heard drilling and hammering?

'Hey all of you,' he croaked with painfully dry tongue. 'Listen!'

Now the others too caught the rattling and knocking in the stone. 'They're there, they're there,' Pierre shouted hoarsely and began knocking in mad haste with a hammer on the black walls. The others followed his example.

Over and over they repeated their knocking signal, listening for an answer. No doubt of it, rescue was on the way. The hammering in the rockface was increasingly audible.

Then the last barriers broke through. Rocks, lumps of coal, broken timbers were cleared away, a man crawled into the gallery, shone a light and stammered: 'It's true, they're still alive.'

Hands stretched out to them. Ambulance men placed the completely exhausted men on stretchers and got them out of the shaft.

In hospital they learned that they had been shut in twelve days and nights and that no one had hoped to get them out alive.

'Amazing that you didn't lose your reason down there!' was the doctor's opinion when he examined them.

'I can explain that all right,' answered digger Farel, and the others agreed. 'We found faith in God again. That alone saved us: otherwise we would have despaired in the end and died — or gone mad.'

---

54. Why do we say: Hallowed be thy Name?

Because we are in awe before the eternal greatness of God.

All by itself?

An American professor tells the story:

I am a biologist. Every day I study the wonders of nature, from simple plant forms to the animals and the human race. I am always astonished over the secrets of creation.

I have a friend who is an astronomer. He spends many a night behind his telescope studying the millions of stars and the planets.

One night he took me with him stargazing. He pointed out a little bright fleck in the sky and then invited me to look at it through the giant telescope. It was a breathtaking picture. The bright fleck revealed itself as an unbelievable wealth of big and little stars in the shape of a gigantic spiral.

The astromoner explained: 'That is a galaxy with about a thousand million stars.'

Then I felt very small, overwhelmed by the greatness of creation.

'Who made all these stars?' I had to ask my friend.

His opinion was: 'No one. They came about by themselves.' My friend is in fact an atheist. He does not believe in God.

Shortly afterwards I invited him to supper. In my living-room hangs a mobile: the sun and all its planets.

My friend was in an ecstasy of admiration. 'That is something,' he said. 'Each planet is going on its right path round the sun. That is really well done. Who made it?'

I smiled at him and answered: 'No one. It came of itself.'

---

55. Why do we ask: 'Thy kingdom come'?

So that there may be more love and justice on earth.

The papal car

In India there are some four million lepers. The leper is an outcast, in many cases simply driven away from home. For this reason people suffering from leprosy do everything possible to hide the fearful disease.

Mother Teresa of Calcutta wanted to overcome this prejudice. She dreamed of a 'peace town' where the lepers would be healed. But unfortunately she had no money for it.

One day she heard that the Pope was to come to India for the first time. Pope Paul VI did indeed go to Bombay in 1964. The enthusiasm of the Indian people was surprisingly great.

An American firm sent him a wonderful white car. In this car he drove from the airport to the city centre of Bombay. At the end of his visit he presented the car to Mother Teresa, the mother of the poor, for her 'unbounded works of love' as he said. What was she to do with it? Mother Teresa knew very well what to do. She organised a lottery. The white car was the first prize. A widow bought ten tickets in the hope of winning the beautiful car for her son. She was lucky enough to get the first prize. But she soon realised that the upkeep of the car was too expensive. She sold it again and gave the greater part of the proceeds to Mother Teresa.

Now the dream became a reality. The Indian government granted the use of a large tract of land in the neighbourhood of Calcutta. With the money from the papal car Mother Teresa was able to build many small houses on this site for the lepers. She also built a hospital where many of the sick were cured. She put up workshops where those who had been cured could learn a trade.

So the Pope's gift brought about a whole city of hope. And today everyone knows that in Calcutta, capital city of misery, there is also a 'city of peace' where the lepers are not shunned but cared for, nursed and in many cases cured.

---

56. Why do we say: 'Thy will be done'?

Because God intends the best for us by his commands and precepts.

Bach's favourite song

Johann Sebastian Bach went blind in his old age. One day a friend let him know that a famous eye surgeon had come to the town and had declared himself ready to put his skill at his disposal if he cared to undergo an operation.

'Yes, in God's name,' said the aged Bach. The day came. But the operation was not a success. When, after four long days, the surgeon removed the bandages from his eyes and the loving family standing round asked their father: 'Can you see?' he replied: 'The Lord's will be done. I can see nothing.'

All around wept, so grieving the old father's heart. He called out to cheer them: 'You will do better to sing my favourite song: What my God wills be done always, he knows best.'

---

57. Is God to blame if many do not get their daily bread?

No, it is the fault of the selfish people who deprive others of bread.

Making a show

A 40-year-old Berliner has this to tell:

My husband is not a bad lot, he doesn't drink and does no harm to anybody. But he is a great one for keeping up appearances. Since we married I've had no peace, we are always in want and difficult circumstances and the bailiff is a constant visitor to our house. Whenever there's a ring at the door I think that again it's somebody wanting his money. I can't sleep at night any more for worrying. I always have to be thinking of the children who often don't get enough to eat.

My husband is certainly no great wage earner but he could get by. But for show he had to get a car that was far beyond his means. He couldn't pay and got into debt. Every day he leaves his limousine in front of his office like some managing director only to make a show and his whole paypacket goes on the car. And he's always running up new debts.

At the midday break he goes to a restaurant and we at home have to go hungry. Our son often begs his father: 'Dad, do sell that big car. You'll get us all into trouble.'

But he doesn't think of that, he only thinks of his prestige. What would his colleagues at work say if he came without a car? They would be glad at his expense and laugh at him.

He couldn't bear that. But that we at home never have a happy minute, that simply leaves him cold.

There are such selfish people in many families and in many communities. Likewise in the great family of peoples there are rich countries which leave at most a few crumbs over for the poorest countries. Each of us ought to ask: 'Am I one of these selfish folk?'

---

58. Why do we say: 'Forgive us . . . as we forgive'?

Because only one who is merciful is deserving of God's mercy.

'And yet he forgave me'

The Civil War was raging ruthlessly across Spain. Churches desecrated, villages in flames, mutilated corpses marked the path of the Red Army. And the Nationals too fought with unparalleled doggedness. When one troop of National soldiers had cleared a village of their opponents they found in a corner of a wall a badly wounded Red, his breast pierced by a splinter from a grenade.

With glazed eyes the wounded man watched the approaching patrol. Then he feebly raised a hand and stammered: 'A priest! Fetch me a priest.'

'Go to hell, Red rabble!' cursed one of the Nationals. But one of his comrades had pity: 'I will see if I can find a priest.'

And indeed he did return with a priest who bent compassionately over the wounded man, a youngster in the prime of life.

'You want to confess?' he asked him.

'Yes I want to confess,' gasped the soldier. 'But tell me, are you the priest of this place?'

'Yes I am.'

'My God!' stammered the boy.

It was a long time before the priest left the dying man. His hair was soaked in sweat and his face white as the wall when he returned to the waiting patrol.

'Brothers,' he told them, 'take the wounded man into the nearby house so that he does not die in the street.'

When the soldiers approached the young man he raised himself a little and signed to them.

'He forgave me! He gave me absolution,' he gasped, struggling for breath.

'Why shouldn't he forgive? That's his business,' said one of the Nationals.

'You don't know what I have done,' groaned the dying man. 'On my own I have killed thirty-two priests; I stabbed, shot, struck down, throttled. In every village I forced my way first to the priest's house. I did it here too. The priest was not in, but I found his father and his two brothers. I asked them where the priest was. They refused to betray him. So I shot all three. Do you understand? The priest who heard my confession: I killed his father and his brothers . . . And yet he forgave me.'

---

59. What does it mean: 'Lead us not into temptation'?

It means strengthen our weakness so we do not offend you.

Gone up in smoke

In most of Africa people are still very poor. In the big town of Abidjan in the Ivory Coast there are thousands of abandoned children. Their parents have nothing themselves and cannot feed them. And so many of them end up on the streets where they take to begging or stealing.

In 1960 a young French priest, Fr Martin, began caring for some of these children. He rented a house for them and they were soon calling it 'our home.'

One day the boys brought a new youngster to the Father. He had belonged to a gang of pickpockets. The next evening a man brought a 100 Francs note for the new boy. That was his cut from the latest robbery.

The lad was going to pocket it straight away. But then he wondered whether that was right. He went to Paul, the leader of the boys in the home.

'That's dirty money,' said Paul, 'you ought not to keep it.'

He called the others together and asked what was to be done with the 100 Francs note. One suggested: 'We'll buy a football.' The others wanted to go to the cinema instead.

To that Paul suggested: 'But this money doesn't belong to us,' 'Let's give it back to the owner,' one called out. But they didn't know who the owner was.

Then Paul decided: 'That is stolen money. I tell you, it's dirty money. We should destroy it.'

All agreed. Paul fetched a cigarette lighter and burned the note.

When Fr Martin heard of it he thought: 'And I haven't ten Francs in hand to buy the new boy a sleeping mat!'

The next day he received quite unexpectedly a gift of 1500 Francs. The children saw in this the reward for the way they had withstood the temptation to pocket the dirty money. Fr Martin soon found work for the older boys. When one of them brought his first pay to the Father he said full of pride: 'That is *clean* money.'

---

60. Who can deliver us from evil?

Christ the Saviour of all.

The 'International' in German

Russia, Christmas Eve 1946. In the German Prisoner of War camp all had gone quiet. Dead tired after the heavy work shift in the coal mine, most had stretched out on their bunks, their dirty miner's overalls pulled over their heads so as to drop off quickly into the land of dreams – a golden bridge leading home.

Only a few, undeterred, endeavoured to celebrate Christmas. A few texts and half remembered old carols, that was all. A miner's lamp threw a fitful light through the large room where so much longing and homesickness slumbered that day.

Then the heavy bolted door was suddenly thrown back and the commandant, the most feared by the prisoners, brought them all back to the harsh present. 'All out!' Obviously a roll call, standing for hours in the cold.

From the watchtowers searchlights played on the rows of figures standing freezing. Guards and camp commandant came forward in military great coat and fur hats. An inter-preter was called out to the commandant. Phrase by phrase he translated into German; 'Prisoners of war, today in your country you German reactionaries keep a festival lasting two days. In the Soviet Union we have no time for holidays. We work for the good of the proletariat of the world so that the hour of their deliverance will soon strike. So you will now sing the "International" as a sign of your solidarity with all workers.'

The interpreter was already beginning to lead: 'Condemned of the earth, awake . . .' But the thousand prisoners remained silent. At the back another song began, some taking it up, hesitatingly at first: 'Silent Night, Holy Night . . .' Then they all joined in loud and full. The first verse came to an end. The translator was just repeating the end of the "International": 'Peoples, hear the signal . . .' and out rang the next verse of 'Silent Night' like a challenge and the final words were shouted out by a thousand throats in the stillness of the night: 'Christ our Saviour is born, Christ our Saviour is born.' It resounded as an enthusiastic expression of faith making its way through the triple barb-ed wire stockade and on through the endless Russian steppe.

Then a breathless silence reigned. The commandant put a question to the interpreter. The answer rang out loud: 'That was the "International" to the German tune.'

The Ten Commandments

You shall have no gods except me.
You shall not misuse the name of the Lord your
 God.
Observe the Sabbath day and keep it holy.
Honour your father and mother.
You shall not kill.
You shall not commit adultery.
You shall not steal.
You shall not bear false witness against your
 neighbour.
You shall not covet (that is, set your heart on)
 your neighbour's wife.
You shall not covet your neighbour's goods.

61. Why did God gives us the Ten Commandments as a signpost?

Because he wants to lead his children to the fullness of life.

The blue light

On 3 February, 1959 at 11.12 p.m., 10,000 metres above the North Atlantic, Flight Captain Waldo Lynch took a last look at the flight panel of the Boeing 707. His co-pilot Sam Peters was studying a map. Captain Lynch wanted to stretch his legs a little, thinking the worst was over.

Shortly after leaving Paris they had run into a 120 km/ph headwind. Now they had managed to climb above the storm area. The captain turned on the automatic pilot, took off his headphones and stood up. He was 47 years of age, muscular and in his prime. He clapped Sam on the shoulder to let him know he was going off for a while.

The captain made his way down between the rows of passengers. They had not yet unfastened their seatbelts which they had fastened before the storm. At the back a baby was crying in the arms of its mother. Captain Lynch reassured her: 'It will be better now. Your baby will be able to sleep.'

What happened at that moment is hard to describe, and harder still to imagine. All at once the captain felt the plane's right wing tip. Lynch was lurched against the seats on the right and at the same moment all the lights went out. Then he literally floated in the air for two or three seconds. Finally he found himself lying on the floor. The captain, numbed with shock, thought it was the floor. But he soon realised it was the roof to which he was glued. There was only one explanation: the Boeing was on its back. The plane was dropping like a stone, head first. The screams of the 116 passengers sounded above the noise of the engines.

Captain Lynch had 15,000 flying hours to his credit. So he reacted as a seasoned pilot. He must leave the passengers to it and get straight back to the cockpit. But how could he reach Sam with the force of gravity pressing him against the roof!

Lynch had unbounded energy and with enormous effort he reached one seat rank and so pulled himself from seat to seat towards the cockpit. He heard the droning of the engines, so they were still working. There was a likelihood of saving the plane, but was there time? He knew it was a question of seconds only. The plane must already have dropped some 6,000 metres, as it was back in the middle of the storm. Suddenly Lynch sensed a new movement of the plane: it straightened out then went into a spiral. This time the captain thought: 'That's it!' The Boeing 707 was now only a whirling leaf in the storm. The passengers were no longer screaming, being either unconscious or waiting for death.

But Lynch refused to give in. He had now reached the first class cabin at the front. With what remained of his strength he went on pulling himself from seat to seat. Suddenly the whole plane shuddered. 'Now we're going to break up.' That was the captain's final thought before he was thrown over. The Boeing was no longer turning like a leaf in the wind but was hurtling towards the ocean like a rocket. The howling of the engines was unbearable, the whole cabin was shaken by them. The plane was nearing the speed of sound. But it was no longer in the midst of the storm. The captain found hope again. How many seconds had he still? With a superhuman effort he was able to work himself into the cockpit and felt hands seizing him and hauling him in. It was the mechanic and the navigator. Lynch grasped hold of the pilot seat and was able to get into it. At last he had his hands on the controls. Through the night and the storm he could see the wild sea. He would try to hold the altitude at 2,000 metres. But, in the single second it took him to think that, the plane had already fallen another 300 metres. As Lynch endeavoured to gain height he noticed the co-pilot was unconscious. He cried to the others: 'Help me!' The three men wrestled with the controls as though possessed. But in that vertical descent at the speed of sound they were thrown back at each time; even with their concerted efforts they could not bring it off. And the raging sea was rushing up towards them.

Suddenly the co-pilot came to. The four of them managed to bring the Boeing to the horizontal.

A few more seconds and the plane would have crashed

in the Atlantic. No one was injured. The whole thing had lasted no more than four minutes.

What had gone wrong? The co-pilot had been studying the map and did not immediately notice the blue light on the indicator panel, the warning signal that the automatic pilot had stopped working.

God our Father has given us warning signals too: the Ten Commandments. He has imprinted them in general outline in every human heart. Let us not ignore them! They can save us from many a disaster.

---

62. What are the first three commandments?

No idols, no lip-service, no Sunday without worship of God.

Applause for Stalin (No idols)

In Russia until recently the marxists taught there is no God. But the leaders, especially Lenin and Stalin, were therefore treated like gods. With the result that almost unbelievable things took place. Alexander Solzhenitzyn tells this in his book *The Gulag Archipelago*:

In a small town in the neighbourhood of Moscow a political meeting was being held. On the podium sat the important people of the town.

Among the people in the auditorium were as always plainclothes secret police. Many speeches were given, culminating in a speech in praise of Stalin.

Hardly had the speaker finished than all stood up clapping entusiastically. They clapped and clapped. Three minutes, four minutes. Everyone knew the secret police were observing closely to see who would be the first to stop clapping. But nobody gave up. Six minutes, seven minutes, eight minutes. The older men had palpitations from so much clapping but didn't stop. Nine, ten minutes. Now everyone was fearful: how was it to end? Eleven minutes. For the director of the paper mill standing on the podium it was getting too stupid. He was a courageous man. He stopped clapping and sat down.

During the following week the director was arrested on a charge of mismanagement. He was condemned to ten years imprisonment.

At the end of the trial the judge said to him on the side: 'Next time see that you are not the first to stop clapping if it's for Stalin.'

Of course it is not only the communists who have idols. We have false gods too: obvious ones such as cars, films, clothes, money and also secret ones like pleasure, power, success.

---

63. What is 'lip service'?

Not meaning what we say.

Haselbauer

In Bavaria the following story is told:

Haselbauer was gravely ill and the priest was with him. First came confession. But the priest had to put a few questions because Haselbauer certainly knew many of his neighbour's sins but he had poor recall for his own.

'Now, Haselbauer, have you said any prayers since your last confession?' asked the priest.

'Aye,' came the laconic reply.'

'What prayers then?'

'Our Father.'

'So every day you said: "Forgive us our trespasses as we forgive . . .",' put in the priest firmly.

'Aye.'

'Well then,' suggested the priest, 'have you in fact forgiven all your enemies?'

'Aye − except Hansjörg. He let me down too badly.'

'Haselbauer, no exceptions will do, and once you're dead it will be too late.'

Haselbauer thought the matter over carefully: 'Aye, I forgive him too supposing I die. But things will remain as before if I get better.'

But that won't work!

When we speak to God there can be no 'lip service'. God is not to be mocked.

---

64. What is the sense of Sunday?

To worship God and spend time with our families.

The two wills

This happened in Frankfurt, many years ago. A very wealthy man died. He had no near relatives. Everybody was eager to know: 'Who will have the millions now?'

The man left two wills. One was to be opened immediately on his death, the other only after the funeral.

In the first will it said 'I will to be buried at 4 a.m. tomorrow.'

So this strange wish was carried out. Only five mourners accompanied the coffin.

Then the second will was opened. There it said: 'I will that my whole estate be divided among those who were present at my burial.'

Those five true friends were lucky! We might almost envy them. But basically we have no call to do so. For we are luckier. How so?

Every Sunday we come together because of a last will and testament. The will Jesus left when he said to us: 'Do this in memory of me.'

Many people find this will very strange and stay at home on Sundays. But we know that much more than a million will be given us in during the commemoration of Jesus' act of love. For at Mass we receive the light and the strength which will lead us to everlasting joy.

---

65. What are the next four commandments?

To honour our parents, not to kill, not to commit adultery, not to steal.

All done for nothing (Honouring our parents)

Little Billy was sitting at the kitchen table, his tongue between his teeth, zealously writing in his exercise book.
'What are you so busy writing?' asked his mother.
'A bill for you,' answered the boy without looking up.
'Well, you make me curious,' suggested his mother.
'You'll soon see when I've finished.' When he had filled up the whole page he showed it to his mother who began to read it aloud:

Account rendered by Billy Wood to his mother

3 x fetching the milk	30p
2 x cleaning the kitchen	£1.20
3 x washing up	60p
5 x cleaning shoes	£1.50
4 x laying the table	80p
Total	£4.40

The mother had to laugh on reading the unusual account. Then she picked up a pencil. 'I'll write my bill on the opposite page,' she said.
'Your bill?' asked Billy in amazement. 'Have you done something for me then?'
'Well, just a bit,' nodded his mother. Then she wrote:

Account rendered to Billy Wood by his mother.

8 years cooking for him	0.00
8 years washing	0.00
50 x jackets and socks mended	0.00
100 nights stayed up with him when he was sick	0.00
Total	£0.00

Carefully the little boy read his mother's account. 'But, Mummy, why have you written £0.00 for the lot?'

'Because a mother does everything for her child for nothing,' the woman answered,' but now I'll give you the £4.40 which you did earn.'

So the boy said: 'No, Mummy, I don't want a penny, 'cos your bill must be a hundred times more than mine!'

---

66. Is abortion murder?

Yes, because it is killing the unborn child.

A mother's enforced happiness

A gynaecologist in Tübingen tells of an interesting case:

A young woman came to consult me. She had married a scientist and helped her husband in his work. She told me that she was first time pregnant. But she did not want a child. Could I perform an abortion.

'Can you really not bear a child?' I asked.

'I didn't get married to have children but to help my husband with his scientific work.'

'Perhaps,' I suggested, 'your husband would rather have a child than a research worker.'

'I don't think so,' she replied haughtily, 'and, besides, that is my affair and nothing to do with anybody else.'

'In any case,' I warned her, 'you cannot count on my assistance. And if you try elsewhere, think the matter over carefully first.'

'I have considered it for a long time.'

We sat looking at each other without a word. Then I said to her:

'So you want to kill your own child. You are a murderer!'

She went white with rage at that. She leapt up, seized her handbag and slammed the door behind her.

Seven months later a call came. It was this same woman: 'Can you assist at the birth of my child?' I had to smile to myself.

Of course I went to her help. Then she could not find words enough to express her gratitude for her 'enforced motherhood'.

In the years to come she became the mother of three more children and for years she sent me regular Thank You cards and flowers.

---

67. What does adultery mean?

It means: taking away another's wife or husband.

'You're not my Mummy!'

Nanette, a Frenchwoman, has this account:

I was born in a town on the Atlantic coast and had a happy childhood with my brother and sister.

When I was nine we children were sent to our grand-father's in the country for the holidays. A week later my mother called in. She did not go to the house but slipped into the garden to us and told us: 'Your father doesn't want me to talk to you.' That made a deep impression.

Later we learned that mother had left home that day. Only years later I heard why that was: Mother accused my faher of having relations with other women.

Then the holidays were over. Father came and took us away. I can remember it exactly. He was standing outside by his car. We had our bags and cases. A woman was standing next to Father. 'Come here, children, and greet your new mother.'

I refused to greet her. Father said: 'Oh, that will soon pass.' I still simply couldn't grasp that I hadn't my Mummy any more.

It was like a thunderbolt when I was told: 'Your parents have divorced. You have a new mother.' I couldn't take that. It was too much for me.

Because of my attitude, my stepmother hated me too. I would not obey her. I grew more and more bitter and withdrawn. My personality changed.

My stepmother and my father were very much in love. They often went to the theatre or the opera. We stayed at home, were anxious and told one another: 'You see, they don't love us.'

Once my stepmother struck me, again without cause, and screamed at me: 'You're not my child!' I screamed back: 'You're not my Mummy.'

Years passed, the situation got worse and worse. Then one day came the crunch.

My little sister was very sensitive to hot water. My stepmother had drawn her a hot bath. I put my elbow in and said: 'That water's too hot.' My stepmother heard this and said: 'Get in at once.' She grabbed my sister and plunged her in. My sister screamed with pain. Rage overwhelmed me. I threw myself on my stepmother. She fell backwards and hit her head against the wallcupboard. There she lay unconscious on the ground.

Stiff with fright I thought: 'You've done her in.' In my panic I rushed out of the house and ran off as fast as I could. At the station I got into the train and travelled as far as the terminus, without a ticket.

Then I stood there. Hundreds of people rushed right past in all directions. I must have looked completely lost. Then suddenly a smart young man spoke to me. He had clearly seen the straits I was in. He promised a fine life and plenty of money if I would work with him. I had no choice for I couldn't go back home, for anything. And so I became a call girl, at the age of fourteen.

68. It is only thieves who steal?

No, everyone who keeps back what could be of use to many.

The scandal of hunger

French journalist France Lesprit tells her experience in one of the poorest countries in the world, Bangladesh:

A few days ago I saw a boy laying on the pavement and by him an empty tin plate. That was not unusual as there are hundreds of such poor people in Dacca. But this boy was in the midst of refuse and his last gasp. Around him ravens hopped clearly waiting for him to die.

His ribs stood out, covered in sores, his arms were like a skeleton's and full of festering wounds.

I bent down to offer him something to eat. He turned away; he had come to the point when nothing matters and there is no desire for food. I took him to the home for the dying run by Mother Teresa's Sisters. But it was already too late. The following day he died quietly.

Now we should ask ourselves:
- Why did this boy in Dacca have to die?
- Why must at least 200 people starve to death daily in this city?
- Yes, why must millions in the world go on starving?

We in the rich countries of the world should be concerned. Although we are only twenty per cent of the human race, we use up eighty per cent of the world's resources.

69. What are the three last commandments?

**Not to lie, not to covet, not to
envy others.**

What if a lie is unavoidable?

When all the men in a country are soldiers there are no
workers. In 1943 Hitler needed foreign labour for his
munition factories. So he had many young men from the
occupied regions transported to Germany. Platoons of
soldiers would descend on a residential district and carry
off the young men by force.

A seventeen-year-old Dutchman, Peter van Woerden, tells
how things went when there was one such raid on his family:

One thing was bothering my sister. What should she
answer if the soldiers came by surprise and we brothers had
hidden in the house? Tell the truth? Or make up some lie
for the enemy and save us? On this we were not agreed. Our
mother sat there composedly waiting for the conclusion of
our discussion. Then she repeated: 'Honesty is the best
policy. Be honest, then you can be sure you have the Lord
on your side.'

A few days later it happened. My younger sister Cocky
was just cleaning an upstairs bedroom. When she opened
a window to shake out the duster she saw the soldiers going
from house to house nearby. In distress she ran down the
stairs straight into my arms. 'Peter, quick! Hide! They're
here.'

Under the floor of our kitchen, which had no cellar, we
had made a hole for just such an eventuality. With shaking
hands Cocky lifted the floorboards and helped me into my
hiding hole. Then she laid the planks carefully back and
covered them with a small carpet. Onto that went the table,
which had a tablecloth hanging down low.

I could already hear the heavy tramp of nailed boots above
me. My heart beat so hard I thought its knocking must
betray me. I listened as a man's voice asked in broken Dutch:
'Any lads in the house?'

There it was then, the question for which we had never been able to agree on the answer. What could Cocky do? Tell the truth? That would spell my arrest. But to say no wasn't a lie, was it?

'Lord give her wisdom,' I prayed.

'Any young men in the house? Yes or no!' repeated the soldier.

'Yes, sir,' I heard the clear young girl's voice say. 'Under the table.'

Hastily the soldier lifted up the tablecloth and looked underneath. Nothing.

Cocky broke out into loud laughter.

The man went red in the face at having let himself be hoodwinked by a slip of a girl and broke off the search.

---

70. What does 'to covet' mean?

It means: we should not keep bad thoughts in our hearts.

The wish is father to the deed

It was 1902, in Italy. Two families lived next door to each other in the country: the Goretti family and the Serenellis.

Mamma Goretti was a widow and had to go out to work on the land along with her sixteen-year-old son in order to feed the five younger children. She could only manage this because twelve-year-old Maria had taken over the housework. She was a pretty, hardworking, cheerful girl.

In the Serenelli family things were different. Their father drank and had paid little attention to the upbringing of his twenty-year-old son Alessandro. He was a good for nothing who gave a wide berth to any honest work. He fancied the neighbours' good-looking girl.

One day he called Maria up to his room. He tried to persuade her to submit herself to his wishes, and became more and more pressing. Maria however remained firm. In his unbounded disappointment the young man grew angry. He seized a knife to threaten her. When Maria screamed out for help he lost all self-control. He threw himself on her and plunged the knife several times into her body.

Maria died a few days later in hospital after much suffering. Shortly before her death she forgave he murderer.

'Blessed are the pure of heart for they shall see God' (Matthew 5:8).

What can we do about impure thoughts?

Don Bosco suggests: If it occurs during the day take up some work or other at once, but if at night do not cease praying until you are overcome by sleep.

So Don Bosco recommends two things: distracting our attention and prayer.

But how are we to pray? The best thing is to pray so as to be distracted. For example, we can pray for the different people in the world and, for instance, name a country at each breath:

'Lord, help England
           France
           Germany
     help China
           India
           Japan.'

When you run out of countries take towns and villages instead.

We should go on doing that as long as necessary — and begin again calmly and firmly as often as necessary.

In that way the temptation become a blessing for countless people in other parts of the world.

The Sacraments

Human beings need tangible signs. How are we to believe ourselves loved, for example, when no sign of love is given . . . even if it is only a smile?

And so God also has given to the faithful tangible signs of his love — above all the seven sacraments. Through them we receive the fullness of the divine love. This life of the soul develops in the same way as the life of the body.

Baptism is birth.
Confirmation is reaching maturity.
The *Eucharist* is food.
The *Sacrament of Reconciliation* is a remedy.
The *Anointing of the Sick* is healing.
The *Priesthood* is ministry to the people of God.
The sacrament of *Matrimony* is growth.

71. What is Baptism?

It is a purification which makes us children of God.

Helen Keller

Helen Keller lost sight and hearing when she was eighteen months old. So she was deaf, dumb and blind. How could a grown woman, open to the world, develop from that poor child who was buried alive, as it were? Helen Keller tells us herself:

When I was six my desire to make myself understood grew from day to day. Since I could not break through this wall of silence surrounding me I grew more and more enraged by it. It was as though invisible hands were holding me back and I made despairing efforts to free myself. Usually my outbreaks of anger ended in my escaping completely exhausted and in tears to the arms of my mother.

My parents were deeply worried and totally at a loss about what to do. However after long searching they found help.

The most important day of my life was the one on which my teacher, Miss Sullivan, came. It was 3 March 1887, three months before my seventh birthday.

The morning after her arrival Miss Sullivan took me to her room and gave me a small doll. When I had played with it for a while Miss Sullivan slowly spelt out d-o-l-l in the palm of my hand. This finger game interested me at once and I began to imitate it. When I had at last succeeded in imitating the letters exactly I flushed with joy and childish pride. I ran downstairs to my mother, stretched out my hand and showed her the letters I had just learned to make. I did not yet know at the time that I was spelling a word nor even that words existed; I simply moved my fingers in imitation. In this way I learned to spell a whole lot of words.

But it was not until a few weeks later that the miracle happened. It was like this:

We had had an argument over the words w-a-t-e-r and

m-u-g. Miss Sullivan had tried to convince me that m-u-g was the container and w-a-t-e-r what was in it but I persisted in confusing the two. In desperation she let the matter drop.

She fetched me my hat and I knew that now we were to go out into the warm sunshine. The thought of it made me hop and skip for joy.

We took the path through the scented lilacs to the well. Someone was pumping water and my teacher held my hand under the spout while the cool stream splashed over my one hand and she spelt out in the other w-a-t-e-r, slowly at first and then quickly. I stood still and excitedly followed the movement of her fingers.

All at once a flash of realisation went through me — and the secret of language lay open to me: everything had a name!

I knew now that water meant the wonderful cool something streaming over my hand. This living word awoke my soul to life, gave it light, hope and joy, freed it from its bonds.

I left the well full of the desire to learn. Every thing had its name.

That day I learned a whole crowd of new words. I do not remember them all but I know that among them were mother, father, sister — words which brought the world to life for me.

Helen Keller was freed from her narrow prison through *water*, the water flowing over her hand.

'This living word,' she wrote, 'awoke my soul to life, gave it light, hope and joy, and freed it from its bonds.'

So does Baptism awaken our soul to new, divine life and free it from the bonds of original sin.

72. How is the Christian made firm in Confirmation?

The laying of hands by a bishop fills a person with the Holy Spirit.

Confirmation means holding fast

In Russia the communists wanted by every means to destroy the faith. Here is the letter of a Christian schoolgirl in Lithuania:

When I was in fifth form the class teacher tried to force me to join the Pioneers. The Pioneers are the communist youth movement. When he saw me hesitate he said: 'If you refuse this year, next year you'll have to.' As later on I still refused he threatened me with bad marks and other punishments. Soon I had to realise that he spoke in earnest. My marks from some of the teachers got worse and worse.

On one occasion I met the teacher in the street. He asked me: 'Where are you going?' I answered: 'I'm going to church.' Then he warned me: 'Just you put a stop to this running off to church.'

One day questionnaires were given out in class. The questions were:
− Do you go to church?
− Who sends you to church? etc.
I answered the questions as follows:
− Yes, I go to church.
− I go to church because I want to.

Shortly afterwards the teacher called me over and said: 'So you're still going to church. Go then! But mind this: when the government people come and ask you whether you go to church and whether you believe, you must answer no.' I spoke about this at home to my parents and they counselled me never to lie to God.

In class we had to write essays against religion regularly. And so the teacher tormented me all through the school year about my faith.

That was a courageous girl.

A Christian has not only to accept the faith but also to grow in it in order to stand firm under mockery and persecution. So we see what a good thing it is for a young Christian to receive the necessary strength from on high in the Sacrament of Confirmation.

---

73. What happens at Mass?

Jesus' sacrifice on the cross is offered to the Father for our salvation.

Willing to die

It was during the Second World War. Throughout Europe the Jews were hunted down, deported and murdered.

Jewish resistance fighters tried desperately to free their imprisoned brethren. By night they made lightning attacks on the dreaded SS. Wittenberg was the leader of these bold resistance fighters in Vilna. The SS had put a high price on his head.

One day he was taken. But the SS rejoiced too soon. Wittenberg was able to escape and go underground in the Jewish quarter of Vilna.

When the SS general heard that, he ordered the whole of the Jewish quarter to be closed off under strict guard. Then he sent a message to the Jews: Either Wittenberg is handed over or all inhabitants will be transported to extermination camps.

A dull fear lay over the unfortunate folk. But Wittenberg lifted it. They should not meet their end on his account. From mouth to mouth ran the news: 'He's giving himself up.'

When the time came both sides of the street leading to the town gate were lined with Jews: on one side the young fighters, on the other old men, women and children.

Wittenberg commissioned a man called Korner as his successor and gave him his pistols.

Then he strode down the empty roadway to the gate not looking to right or left. Bravely he went to a fearful death.

Jesus too went of his own free will to a fearful death. he did it to save us all. This sacrifice of the God-man, made once, has infinite value. In every Mass this same sacrifice is offered to God the Father for our sins.

---

74. How should we receive Jesus in Holy Communion?

With a firm faith which expects everything from him.

A reward for trust

One day the Emperor Napoleon went to an inn. He was accompanied only by his adjutant. They did not want to be recognised and so were not in their usual clothes.

After the meal the old landlady brought the bill for 14 Francs. The adjutant took out his purse and went pale for his purse was in fact empty.

The emperor smiled condescendingly and said: 'Don't worry about it. I'll pay.' He went through his pockets but had to admit that he had not a Franc on him.

What were they to do? The adjutant made the landlady a proposition: 'We have come without our money. But I will return within an hour and pay you.'

The old woman would not hear of it. She threatened to fetch the gendarmes on the spot if she was not paid at once.

The waiter, who had been following the argument, felt sorry for the two gentlemen. He spoke to the landlady: 'Why, that can happen to anyone, coming out without money. Don't do anything about the gendarmes. I'll pay the 14 Francs for them. They seem honest men.'

So they were able to leave the place.

The adjutant soon came back and said to the landlady: 'How much did you pay for this inn?'

'30,000 Francs,' the old woman answered.

He took out his wallet and counted out 30,000 Francs onto the table. Then he explained: 'On the emperor's orders I am to present this inn to your waiter who helped us in our need.'

Now we can ask ourselves: How did the landlady lose her inn and why was the waiter so well rewarded? Both took in the same eminent guest and attended to his needs. But the difference between them is great: the waiter trusted the unsuspected guests, the landlady did not.

We too receive Christ as our guest under the guise of the host. How is it that some draw profit from this and others do not?

It comes from the fact that some put their trust in him but others do not. Some expect absolutely everything from him, others are indifferent and expect nothing.

---

75. How can we be rid of our sins?

By repenting of them and confessing them.

The stolen diamond

A remarkable story is told of a king of Aragon in Spain:

One day the king went with his courtiers to a jeweller's. While he was conversing with the dealer the courtiers were inspecting the jewellery.

After they left the shop the jeweller came running behind very upset. He informed the king that a costly diamond was missing. The king commanded his suite return to the shop. He told the jeweller to get a jug filled with salt. Then he ordered his retinue to plunge their fists into the jug in turn and draw them out with their hands open.

When all had done this the salt was poured onto the table. Lo and behold the diamond appeared.

113

This king was generous. He wanted to give the thief the opportunity to make good his dishonesty without being put to shame.

And that is how Jesus Christ acts with us. So long as we are on earth we can always receive his forgiveness under the seal of the Sacrament of Reconciliation.

---

76. Why should we repent of our sins?

Because by our sins we have offended God.

Robbery with manslaughter

Portugal 1910:

Midnight had just sounded from the tower of the parish church in the town. Fr Ribeira got up from his chair to leave his study when there was a ring at the doorbell. Probably a sickcall, he thought.

When he opened the door a man stepped in, his hat pulled down over his eyes, and said briefly: 'I want to go to confession.'

In spite of the late hour the priest answered: 'By all means.'

In the parlour the man declared: 'I accuse myself of robbery and manslaughter.'

The priest looked at him sharply: 'And are you sorry for it?'

'Oh yes, it was a mistake. I shouldn't have done it at the station. It meant that somebody saw me and called the police.'

'But is it nothing to you that you have offended God?' warned the priest.

'Not at all.'

'Then I cannot give you absolution.'

'No matter. The main thing is you have to hold your tongue — you can't report my crime because of the secret of the confessional. And besides I'll leave my pistol with the stolen wallet here. I'll fetch it later. Adios!'

The man jumped out of the window to the garden and disappeared into the night.

He was scarcely gone when there was a furious ring at the bell. The priest had only the time to push the wallet and pistol under his papers before opening the door.

A couple of armed police walked in and the officer in charge said without preamble: 'Near the station an hour ago a man was robbed and murdered. We have followed the trail here with bloodhounds. What have you to say about the matter?'

'I know nothing about it,' stammered the priest, pale as death.

'You seem to have a bad conscience,' snarled the lieutenant. 'We have to search your residence.'

It was not long before the money and the weapon were found.

'How did these get here?' asked the policeman.

'I have nothing to say,' replied the priest.

'Don't talk rubbish. You are under arrest.'

Fr Ribeira was condemned to life imprisonment with hard labour for robbery and manslaughter.

Six years later during the First World War a badly wounded soldier was brought into a field hospital. He asked for a priest. After his confession he declared before three officers that he was the murderer in whose place Fr Ribeira had been falsely convicted.

So the priest was freed after six years' forced labour, his innocence proven.

77. What happens at the Anointing of the Sick?

The sick person is anointed with oil to gain strength.

'I renounce all'

'No priest at a deathbed.' That was the new law of the freemasons. This secret society is very active since the last century.

Verhaegen, Grand Master of the Belgian freemasons, had cunningly thought up how to ensure the new law: so that in future no sick freemason could receive the visit of a priest, three other freemasons were to remain by his bed.

Next Verhaegen meant to introduce the new law into France and Italy. For this he journeyed from town to town and spoke successfully on the subject.

When he was returning from Italy he had to cross the Alps in severe winter weather. By coach, sledge and mule he at last reached the Mont-Cenis pass. Half frozen, he went into the inn and ordered a hot drink.

The girl brought him a glass of grog. Verhaegen could hardly wait for it. Hastily he swallowed the grog down. Suddenly there was a cry and Verhaegen sprang up with an oath. The drink had been burning hot and he had not noticed. His throat, gullet and stomach were scalded.

With the greatest speed he made the journey to Brussels. The best doctors in the town were called in at once. But all they could do was to shake their heads doubtfully. There was nothing more to be done for him.

On the second day after his arrival in Brussels Verhaegen lost all hope of recovery, seeing the three freemasons who came unbidden into his room. They kept guard with stony faces, speaking no word. And disgust swept over Verhaegen at this religion of darkness and soon after an immense longing for the religion of his childhood, for the Church of Christ.

He called for a priest but the three watchers had barred

the door and no priest came. So Verhaegen died without absolution, unfortified by the Last Sacraments.

On the day of his burial, traces were found of his lonely death struggle. On the wallpaper he had scratched with his fingernail: 'I renounce all and I repent. Verhaegen.'

---

78. What is the task of the ordained priest?

To further Christ's work of salvation by word, by the sacraments and by his example.

On the Donau Canal

In 1950 the Russians wanted to construct a gigantic canal through Romania. This was to be a connecting waterway between Donau and the Black Sea. The communists were very proud of it.

Two hundred thousand prisoners worked on it. Each had to dig out eight cubic metres of earth daily with hand tools. Under the blows of overseers they dragged laden handcarts up steep cliffs. In winter the temperature fell to minus 25 degrees centigrade.

And yet even in this hell beautiful things occurred.

A young catholic priest, Fr Cristea, was an object of particular hatred to one 'squeak'. This man asked him:

'Why do you have your eyes closed? Are you praying? I order you to tell me the truth. Do you still believe in God?'

An affirmative would at the least mean cracks with the whip. However Fr Cristea did not hesitate: 'Yes, I believe in God.'

The 'squeak' hastened to the lieutenant. He came over and ordered the priest to step forward. Fr Cristea was thin and exhausted. He was shivering in his ragged clothes. The lieutenant was well-fed, wrapped in a cloak and wearing a Russian fur cap.

'I hear you believe in God,' he said.

Fr Cristea answered: 'When I was ordained I already knew that many priests had paid for their faith with their lives. Each time I went up to the altar I said to God: I am serving you now in beautiful surroundings but even if I have to be thrown into prison I will still serve you. Lieutenant, prison is no argument against faith. I believe in God.'

The silence then was broken only by the sound of the wind. The lieutenant seemed to be at a loss for words. Finally he said: 'And do you stand by the Pope?'

The answer was: 'Since St Peter there has always been a Pope and there will always be one until Jesus Christ comes again. Yes I stand by the Pope.'

Fr Cristea was shut up in solitary confinement for a week, where there was room only to stand and it was impossible to sleep. He was also severely beaten. He still refused to deny his faith. He was taken away. Nothing has been heard of him since.

---

79. What is effected by the partners' consent in the Sacrament of Matrimony?

Man and woman are bound together indissolubly.

Until death

Katharina Jagello was the wife of Duke Wasa of Poland. When he was condemned to life imprisonment for treason she asked the Swedish King Eric to be allowed to share in her husband's incarceration. The king was horrified and tried to dissuade her.

'Do you realise that your husband will never see the light of day again?'

'That I know, Your Majesty.'

'And do you realise that he will no longer be treated as a duke but as a traitor?'

'Yes, that I know; but whether free or in prison, guilty or not guilty, he remains my husband still.'

'But, after all, you are no longer bound to him. You are free again now.'

Katharina drew her wedding ring from her finger and handed it to the king: 'Read there, Your Majesty. There are but two Latin words engraved within the ring: *Mors sola*. Death alone can part us.'

Katharina went to prison with her husband and for seventeen years shared the hardships and privations with him, until King Eric died and her husband was freed.

---

80. How can we know when love is genuine?

By the way in which it seeks the true happiness of the other.

Heart of gold

An old retired judge was taking his evening walk. He met a young acquaintance.

'Good evening, Paul,' said the old man, 'I hear you are soon to be married. That's grand. Tell me something about your fiancée.'

'Oh, she's a fine girl,' said the young man, 'pretty as a picture.'

The judge pulled a notebook out of his pocket and wrote a nought.

'What else?'

'And she's very clever too.'

The judge entered another nought.

'She'll be getting a good job in the autumn.'

Again a nought. And so it went on until there were six of them.

'Besides,' said Paul, 'my bride-to-be has a heart of gold. I've often noticed that she's always around when help is needed.'

So the judge wrote the figure 1 in front of the six noughts and closed his little book. Then he shook the young man heartily by the hand.

'I congratulate you, Paul. Your bride is worth a million. You can venture your whole life with her.'

Love of God

What is the No. 1 problem the modern Samaritans have to deal with? *Loneliness.*

How up to date St Thomas Aquinas is here: All reasonable laws have one end in view, to foster peace and harmony.

Human laws are meant to further friendly relations between people.

Divine precepts are meant to further friendly relations between God and individuals.

But how is it possible for the infinitely great God and his little human creature to be friends? It is possible because God became man and sent his Spirit.

81. Can we love God without believing his saving message?

No, as we only love what we know to be worthy of love.

Edison

In Michigan, U.S.A., storm and rain had been raging. Streams turned into rushing rivers.

At Mount Clement station a message in morse code was just coming in. Connors, the station master, turned pale.

'The bridge is down,' he called to his colleague. 'Train no. 7 will be there in ten minutes. That is dreadful! They will all perish.'

The fifteen-year-old apprentice listened aghast. If only there was more time. But already the clock showed only nine minutes. All at once he jumped up.

'My sister is on train no. 7. She was meant to be coming home this evening. If I could only get to her!'

Connors shook his head. 'It is too late. The train has already left the last station. My God, it will be frightful!'

The young man was not paying attention. His mind was working feverishly.

'Now I've got it! Quick! A steam engine! I need a steam engine at once to go towards the bridge. I'll send my sister a message by means of the steam whistle. My sister understands morse.'

The station master hesitated. 'But no one will believe your sister.'

'Only eight minutes left,' cried the boy. 'Quick, it's our last chance.'

Connors decided to try it. He called up the fireman of an engine that was being brought in to the sheds.

'Jack, take the lad with you and make for the bridge at full steam. But take care! The bridge is down.'

Edison jumped onto the engine and off they went. Connors watched it disappear round the bend and looked at the clock: only four and a half minutes.

A mile away from the bridge Edison began pulling on the whistle lever as though possessed. At speed the shrill notes came out in morse signals: Bridge down – stop. Bridge down – stop.

In train no. 7 people were talking unconcernedly. Then an old gentleman remarked: 'There's an engine driver who must have gone off his head.' But a young woman was listening attentively.

'Those are morse signals,' she cried, and then she spelled them aloud: 'Bridge d-o-w-n--s-t-o-p. Stop! We must stop the train! The bridge is down!'

The old gentleman got annoyed. 'That's no game to play, young lady. The train stops only in emergency.'

Clearer still the despairing signals could be heard. Only half a mile from disaster.

'But it's not a game,' screamed the girl. 'The bridge is down. We must stop at once. Those are morse signals. I recognise them.'

She tried to pull the emergency chain but she was too short. In despair she buried her face in her hands.

At that an elegantly dressed woman interposed: 'It's quite mad. It can't be true.'

But the old gentleman was impressed. 'Are you sure?' he asked the girl.

'Quite sure. Do be quick!'

So the man jumped up and tugged on the communication cord. The wheels screeched fearfully. The train came to a halt.

They were just ten yards from the abyss.

One thing in this story can give us something to think about. If the old gentleman had not believed the message, he and all his fellow passengers would have been lost.

When we recognise that God has spoken to us and in spite of that we refuse to believe his saving message, then it could happen that we – through our own fault – are lost.

82. What is God's saving message?

Jesus loves us and waits for our love in return.

Nicky Cruz in Berlin

Berlin 1982. In front of 80,000 people gathered in the Olympic Stadium Nicky Cruz was telling the story of his life:

I was eight when my mother threw me out. She said I was a child of the devil and she didn't love me. That hurt so much that I thought: I'll never love again and I'll never cry again.

As I grew up in New York I became leader of a gang of youths: the Mau Mau.

We shot down at people from the roofs, fought with other gangs and were always being held by the police. My gang — there were three hundred of us — was feared throughout New York. They all respected me as I was fearless and hard on my enemies.

Then one day something happened.

I had taken the gang to a disco. I was just dancing with my girl when the door opened and in walked David Wilkerson. David was a small country priest who sometimes did open-air preaching in our quarter. I couldn't stand him. When I saw him I was seized with rage. What was he doing here? I went over to him and struck him in the face. 'Preacher,' I yelled at him, 'get out of here if you value your life.' Then David said: 'Very well, I'm going. I just wanted to say to you: Nicky, Jesus loves you. Jesus loves you.'

And he was gone.

For a whole fortnight I was haunted by those words day and night: 'Jesus loves you.' Then when I heard that David was to speak to young people I put my revolver in my pocket and went to the meeting.

David said things that I have never heard before, that Jesus had suffered everything for us when he fell into the hands of his enemies. I knew just what it meant to fall into enemy hands. David told how Jesus' enemies had treated him. How they beat him cruelly, spat on him and crucified him.

I got worked up. I thought to myself: If I'd been there with my Mau Mau that wouldn't have happened. We'd have fetched him out. But David said that Jesus *wanted* to suffer to pay for our sins.

I was thunderstruck. Could it be true? How could Jesus love me like that? But then I knew: Anyone ready to suffer so much must really love.

So I had a talk with Jesus.

'Jesus do you love me? Do you really love me, just as I am? Oh, Jesus, if you really love me then I will love you too. I will give my whole life to you.'

Hardly had I said that than the hell of bitterness and hate in my heart was wiped away. I was free, free as a bird in the sky.

---

83. Has Jesus said how we can love him?

Yes. He said: One who keeps my commandments is one who loves me.

Who's on the line?

This is the story of Rosie:

When I was a girl I worked in an army canteen. One of my workmates was a big fine man called William. He was always very friendly with me and I liked him a lot. Before we knew what was happening we fell madly in love. Unhappily William was married with three children. But I couldn't imagine life without him. I managed it so that he left his family and joined me. Soon we had twins, both girls, Margaret and Denise. So William had to keep two families. But he hadn't the means. His health was not good and worries and troubles didn't help. Soon I was pregnant again, and William died of a heart attack just before the child was born.

It was another girl and I called her Judy. As soon as the hospital nurse put her in my arms I felt tremendous love for her. She was part of me, my little Judy.

But it was a terrible time. I had to work hard and when I came home after fetching my three children from the playschool I was so exhausted that all I could do was lie on the floor and let them climb over me.

The money gave out. My strength gave out. From all sides people said to me: 'The baby is too much for you. Give her up to be adopted.' That tore at my heart.

But what else could I do? My health was gone. I was in continual depression. I could no longer tell what was real from what I was dreaming. Through an organisation the social worker had found a family who wanted to adopt a child. I gave in and signed – and my little Judy was gone.

It was a hard struggle to bring up the twins alone. They never had anything new to wear and I had neither time nor energy to play with them or tell them stories. Through a chance remark from a neighbour's wife they learned when they were nine that they had a little sister.

They asked me where she was and I had to admit I didn't know. So they began crying inconsolably. 'Our little sister is lost.' For me it was a wound that never healed. On her birthday and at Christmas my thoughts were with Judy. Was she all right? Was she happy?

Years passed. A new law came into effect enabling adopted children to trace their real parents as soon as they were eighteen.

On Judy's eighteenth birthday I could hold out no longer. I got the train for London as I knew she most probably lived there. It was the first time I had been in that great city. I went from one place to another in the hope of getting my daughter's address. In the early hours I would sleep for a while at the station and then go on searching. When I returned home I was dead beat.

Repeatedly I wrote to the adoption organisation that had arranged for Judy. But they would give me no details: Judy had the right to look for me, but not the other way round. I did not want to interfere in my daughter's affairs but I could find no rest day or night till I knew whether she was happy.

126

A few years later I learned that a social worker named John Stroud quite often wrote in the paper about families in difficult situations. He had taken my case to heart and soon found out where Judy lived. She had married happily in the meantime and had a three-year-old girl of her own.

Of course John had told me nothing of this. He had to know first whether my daughter would want to see me. She was overjoyed. Judy said to him: 'All these years I've thought about my family — and now I shall find them.' But she wanted to ask her adoptive parents first. They could not have been more generous and gave her their full consent.

Judy called her family; only Margaret was at home.

'Who is speaking?' asked Margaret.

'It's Judy, your little sister.' No answer came. All Judy could hear was someone sobbing at the other end of the line. Margaret could hardly get a word out. So Judy just said she would phone her mother at 7 p.m.

For me it was overwhelming to hear my daughter's voice. 'Mummy, it's me, Judy.' There was a wonderful reunion.

Now we visit her two or three times a year. Judy gets on fine with her two sisters. She was even mistaken by a neighbour for her sister Denise; they are so alike. I am at peace now. Yes, since Judy has forgiven me I know God has forgiven me. For I greatly offended God, not by giving Judy away but by taking William from his family.

Sometimes I see William's wife out shopping. I always want to say something to her but so far I've not had the courage. Perhaps I shall come to it some day.

84. Why does the cross have more to teach than all the books in the world?

Because it is a sign of the greatest possible love: love even to the supreme sacrifice.

A Russian legend

Two dangerous criminals guilty of many violent robberies were converted by a hermit. They both confessed their many crimes and asked what reparation they could make.

The man of God said they should go on pilgrimage to the Holy Land and in addition carry a heavy cross on their backs. Soon the big crosses were ready and the new converts set off.

All went well at first. The crosses were indeed heavy but they had strength enough. But after a few days their shoulders were sore from the continual chafing of the rough wood.

Then they had an idea how to improve the crosses. They stopped in a village and went to a carpenter's work shop. One sawed off the bottom end of the long arm of the cross and said: 'Now it's much shorter and it's still a cross.' The other did not want to make his cross shorter, only thinner. He sawed it through lengthwise and so made two crosses out of it. One of these he left lying on the ground. Then he said: 'Now it is much lighter and it's still a cross.'

So they were able to get along much better. And that was just as well because they soon came to a rocky desert where they could find nothing to eat. They had to go for three days without a bit of food. On the fourth day they saw a city on the horizon and rejoiced. They walked as fast as they could in their weakened condition.

Towards evening they came up to an unexpected obstacle. A deep canal barred their way. And there was no bridge to be seen. They were exhausted and in despair as neither could swim. Then one had an idea: We can use our crosses as a makeshift bridge. But, you see, one cross was too short. The other was long enough but too thin. So they both perished miserably.

We too are sometimes tempted to halve our crosses.
But the Lord did not carry his cross by halves. He carried the whole of it to the end.

---

85. Can we love God and hate people, who are his children?

No, since when we love someone we love their children too.

Friend or foe?

A Frenchwoman tells her experience during the allied attack on occupied France:

It was on the night of 5 June 1944. I was eleven years old at the time and was with my family sitting in the kitchen late at night. Ours was a lonely house right outside the village. All was quiet along the coastal region of Normandy.

Suddenly we heard the droning of planes. There must have been many of them. Five minutes went by. All at once the kitchen door was thrown open and a man with a black camouflaged face threatened us with a machine gun. We all started up, more out of astonishment than fear.

'Friend or foe?' cried the man, his American accent easily recognisable. To this my five-year-old brother said: 'But we're all friends.'

The stranger's features relaxed a little. 'And where have you come from?' asked my father.

'I'm from heaven – by parachute,' grinned the American.
'Is it the invasion we've been waiting for?' cried Father.
'Yes that's it,' answered the American soldier.

Thousands of parachute troops had made the jump that night so that the English and American ships could bring in the troops.

We took in two wounded Americans who had injured

themselves in the drop. One of them had to stay in bed with a broken and infected leg. The other, Kerry, a kindly giant, could hobble around with a badly sprained foot.

When I got up the next morning I saw from my gable window three men coming up to the house. An officer was supporting two severely wounded soldiers. So I rushed downstairs and called my father. He looked out of the kitchen window and said: 'They're Germans. I'll have nothing to do with them.'

But Mother replied: 'Two of them are badly wounded. We must help them. Genevieve, fetch a big bundle of straw. We'll bed them down in the kitchen. And the parachute in the cellar: we'll spread that over the straw for a sheet.' And so we did.

The Germans were already at the door. They were unarmed. 'Madame, this lad has lost a lot of blood,' said the officer beseechingly. Our mother did what she could to treat both the badly wounded men. I made coffee and gave them some.

At that moment Kerry came hobbling into the kitchen. He had no gun with him. He stared and said nothing. Kerry had never seen a German until then. But he realised at once what was up. Kerry and the German officer stood silently observing each other. Then quite spontaneously the German stretched out his hand to the American. Kerry hesitated a split second. His glance encountered my mother's. She nodded slightly. The gentle giant took the outstretched hand. Both men gave each other a long friendly look.

There were now no longer enemies in our house. Only suffering men.

The German and the American got on very well together. Staggered, I watched the two of them. There they were drinking coffee together at the kitchen table. And yet they ought to have shot each other down, finished each other off, as their compatriots were doing outside. But here in our lonely farmhouse it was quite different. It was a house of God's children.

86. Are there good works other than the corporal works of mercy?

Yes. For example: to teach the ignorant, cheer the sad, bear with unpleasant people.

Storytelling as therapy (Cheering the sad)

Once an Irishman died quite unexpectedly and suddenly found himself before the Divine Judge. He was horribly afraid as he had not done much good in his life. There was a whole queue in front of him; all had to give an account of themselves.

Christ looked through his thick book and said to the first: 'It says here: I was hungry and you gave me food. Good. Up you go to heaven.' To the second: 'I was thirsty and you gave me drink.' To the third: 'I was in prison and you visited me.' And so on.

As each one was told to go into heaven the Irishman examined his conscience and each time he trembled: he had neither given anyone food or drink nor had he visited any prisoners or sick people.

Now it was his turn. He watched Christ go through his book and trembled with fear. But Christ looked up and said: 'There's not much here. But you did do something: I was sad and you told me funny stories. I was depressed and you made me laugh. You cheered me up. Into heaven with you!'

Even if this story is invented it still makes clear that we should not let an opportunity pass for showing love and making others cheerful.

87. Why did God want his children to be dependent on one another?

So that they may live in love, that is, in God.

What a mother can do!

A thirty-year-old Italian tells this:

My sister and I live in the same part of town. And yet it isn't often we see each other.

My mother always asks the same thing in her letters: 'When was the last time you saw your sister?' When once I had to write back 'three months ago' our mother decided to act.

And so, shortly afterwards I had a queer letter in the post. It was from Mother sending me pages one and three of the letter which was directed to us both. Then I knew: my sister had the missing pages two and four.

Since then we each get half a letter every month. And on that account we enjoy spending an evening together each time. Only a mother could think of that!

88. What does it mean: 'You (Christians) are the light of the world'?

It means: Your goodness shows the Father's goodness.

Vladimir, an Orthodox Christian

Vladimir Lindenberg was a doctor in Bonn during the thirties. As an opponent of Hitler he was sentenced to four years of hard labour. Listen to his own account of an overseer in that prison camp:

We called him 'Flabby'. He had a fine riding whip and used it diligently. For choice he hit at our legs. That hurt dreadfully. The whip whistled and you felt a sharp pain; often the skin broke and bled. He made as if he wasn't doing any harm, just like boys inflicting pain on a defenceless animal. Then he would pass on in search of another victim.

When I stopped digging once to get my breath Flabby leapt at me ready to give me a cut with the whip. I had not heard him coming and stood up in surprise. At that moment Flabby looked into my face and stared. At first he didn't know what to say, then he cried: 'D'you know, you're so like somebody I know.'

I only said: 'I don't know who.'

He wouldn't leave off: 'But I must know you. Were you in Bonn once?'

'Yes.'

'Are you a doctor?'

'Yes, I am.'

'Then you saved my wife's life! Don't you remember? I came to your house one night. My wife had terrible stomach pains and I went wildly from one doctor to another and couldn't find any in, or they wouldn't open to me. Then I came to you. You opened the door and came at once with me to Endenich. You diagnosed acute appendicitis and as there was no time to lose took her to hospital. She was operated on straight away just before it burst. Then you brought her back home again. But what are you doing here then, in with criminals?'

'As you see I'm working on the Emsländer Moor. And what you call criminals are all teachers and professors, chemists, students, priests and politicians. You can call us criminals. We don't consider ourselves such.'

He was quite confused, his whole view of things collapsed.

After that encounter the overseer was a changed man. Certainly he gave a stroke with the whip in passing but it was against his own boot, and he stopped doing anything to us.

89. Does true love consist in fine words and feelings?

No, in the firm intention of pleasing the loved one.

A love letter

A young lad is writing a love-letter to his beloved:
'I love you so-o much. I would go through fire and water for you. I would climb the highest mountain, swim the widest river. So I'll come tomorrow evening *if it's not raining.*'

Our love for God should not consist in grand words!

90. Which is the most important decision in a person's life?

It is to choose between self-love and love of God.

A folk tale from Africa

At the beginning of the world God created the flowers, trees, animals and humans. When he had finished that and wanted to have a rest he heard a little voice shrilling loudly, piercing and insistent: 'Pi-i-yip! Pi-i-yip!' So he looked around and caught sight of a red bird swinging on a blade of grass.
'I'm not at all satisfied, great God,' peeped the little bird, 'There's that old cat you know that's always chasing me.'
'If you like,' said God, 'I'll change you into a cat.'
The small bird agreed and in a twinkling he turned into a big cat with long whiskers and sharp claws. 'I'm a hand-

134

some cat,' he thought and gave a loud miaow. Then a dog came along and chased him off. 'Lord,' cried the cat now, 'I can't stand this. That beastly dog!'

So God sighed and said: 'If you like I'll change you into a dog.'

And so it was: the cat became a dog, big and strong with a hefty tail and a powerful bark. And he at once fought with the other dogs and sought out a master to feed him. But when evening came and night lay over the land the dog cowered with fear and began whimpering. There were so many shadows in the night and so many glowing eyes.

'Lord, the lion will be coming and eating me up,' he whimpered. 'Make me into a lion so that I am no longer afraid.'

'By all the stars in heaven,' cried God, 'you're never satisfied! Every minute you want to be something else. All right, as you say, be a lion.'

And the dog turned into a lion. A man heard the lion roaring, ran up with a spear and flung it at the beast.

Now the lion wailed: 'Great God, I really didn't deserve that! I would be better off as a soldier.'

'That is not wise,' said God. 'Do you know what you are asking?'

'I know,' growled the lion. 'I would rather be a warrior.'

Then there fell a shaft of lightning from heaven to earth − and a defiant warrior stood in the middle of the kraal, a soldier with shield and spear and feather headdress. The men of the village eyed him enviously, the girls winked at him. The warrior sunned himself proudly in the people's admiration. One day the paramount chief sent word to the warrior to come and fight for him. Then he started considering why he should obey. 'Am I not as big and powerful and handsome and strong?' And he asked God to change him into a chieftain.

'Be a chieftain,' said God, wanting to be left in peace. And now the warrior sat on a big throne as chief and had many beautiful wives around him. Then the counsellors came up and said: 'Great master, ruler of elephants and rhinos, it is time to make sacrifice to the creator of the world for he is mighty and wonderful.'

Then the chief frowned and said: 'What about me? Am

I not somebody? Who brings me a sacrifice? Why do you not bow down before me?' Then God got angry. Claps of thunder rumbled through the chief's kraal; a fierce wind threw counsellors and wives into disorder and swept the ruler from his throne.

When the people came to themselves again they noticed that the chief had disappeared. A little red bird swung outside instead on a thin grass blade and cried: 'Pi-i-yip! Pi-i-yip!' And the people paid no attention to him as they were looking everywhere for their chieftain.

Love of neighbour

Quo vadis?

Where are you going? What are you aiming for?
That is the only important question.
Do you really know that love is the only goal?
That everything must aim for that?
Even something quite small becomes great when done in
love; and something quite important if not done with love
is nothing.

So it is important for our lives to know: what is true love?
How is it to be distinguished from false love? How is it to
be practised?
This chapter hopes to give at least the essential answers.

91. What are the three kinds of love?

Self-centred love, pleasure-seeking love, love of benevolence.

Missing the train (Self-centred love)

Don Bosco is one of the most popular of the Italian saints. In the last century he set up in Turin a huge orphanage and trade school for street boys.

Once he was visiting in the neighbourhood of Alba. In the evening he wanted to return to Turin but he missed the last train. In pouring rain he knocked at the nearest presbytery. The priest opened the door and asked who he was.

'I'm a poor priest from Turin. I've just missed the last train.'

'What is your position in Turin?'

'I have a small suburban parish.'

'Yes. Have you had supper?'

'If you would be kind enough to give me something I would be most grateful.'

'I'm sorry but I've nothing by me. The most I can offer you is bread and cheese.'

'That will suit me very well. Thank you.'

'Do you intend staying the night?'

'You see how it is. . . this pouring rain. . . and the train has gone!'

'Quite, but I've no spare bed.'

'Oh, that's no problem, a couple of chairs will do.'

'If that's the case then please come in. I'm really sorry I've nothing better to offer.'

While the housekeeper was bringing the bread and cheese the priest continued:

'So you're from Turin?'

'That's right.'

'D'you perhaps know a certain Don Bosco?'

'Yes, a little.'

'I've never met him,' said the priest. 'But I've something

I'd like to ask him. D'you think he would help?'
'He's always ready to help others when he can.'
'I was thinking of writing tomorrow to ask whether he could take a child into his orphanage.'
'He certainly will, I can assure you.'
'Really? Are you a friend of Don Bosco's?'
'Yes, indeed, since childhood.'
'Well, can you arrange the matter for me perhaps?'
'Consider it settled in return for your present kindness.'
'But. . . you. . . who are you then?'
'I'm Don Bosco.'
'Don Bosco? You're Don Bosco! Now why didn't you say so at first? But forgive me for not receiving you properly. . . Now who would have thought it! Do leave that cheese, I've just remembered there's something left over from lunch.'

Thoroughly embarrassed and perspiring the priest called his housekeeper, had a clean cloth put on the table and ordered fish, soup and ham omelette. He ran to the cupboard and fetched half a roast chicken and a bottle of good red wine. He could hardly do enough and Don Bosco smiled to himself meanwhile.

After the meal the guest was taken up to a handsome bedroom. The next morning the priest accompanied him to the station uttering ceaseless apologies.

When saying goodbye Don Bosco took his arm: 'Look, Father, let's learn a lesson from what has happened. When we have nothing we can give nothing. When we have a little we can give a little. And when we have much we can give what seems to be the right thing. But let it always be for love of neighbour and not out of self-interest.'

Do cats love mice? (Pleasure-seeking love)

This is a story from a doctor in Munich:

A young gentleman brought his wife to my surgery – still young, blooming and pretty, aged 20 but severely neurotic. He complained to me that his wife was withdrawn, sat the whole day doing nothing but brood moodily.

So I had a long talk with the young woman – I will call her Susanne. It was not easy to get her to talk. But gradually I learned the whole story.

When Susanne was sixteen she had fallen in love with a married man, the 24-year-old Rolf, who worked in the same office. Rolf felt very flattered by the way the young girl adored him, but passed it off as a joke.

Then at an office party it came to the first kiss and so the relationship between the two of them changed. Now they started meeting quite often after office hours. He told her of his unhappy marriage and said he wanted to divorce his wife. She believed it all. When he promised they would be married as soon as he was free she did what she had long wanted to do − gave herself to him.

This unhappy relationship went on for over a year and during that time she waited from day to day to hear he really had the divorce. In the end he admitted to her that his wife completely refused to free him.

Susanne was out of her mind. Because of her affair with a married man she had broken with her parents and found herself in an impossible situation. But she did not give in and decided to fight for her love.

She sought out Rolf's wife and begged her to free Rolf. It then transpired that this woman had no suspicion of her husband's amorous dealings. The shock of this disclosure was equally great for both the women.

The very practical wife decided to file a divorce. But Rolf reacted quite differently from the way Susanne had expected. He loved his wife and was not prepared to give up either wife or children. He reproached Susanne harshly and they parted.

Susanne suffered the consequences. She gave notice and took another job where she got to know her present husband and soon married him.

But then she felt that it was not in her either to forget Rolf or to love this other man.

The reaction to the disappointment she had undergone came late but all the more violently. She became the severely neurotic woman she now is.

In this sad story we see clearly that love for pleasure is no true love. Susanne was prepared to break up Rolf's family, Rolf on his side lied to Susanne, used her inexperience and thereby cold-bloodedly ruined her future life.

Selfish love and lust are only apparent love. They seek in

the other only personal advantage, self-satisfaction. The other is loved as the cat loves a mouse: it wants only to play with it and enjoy it.

First prize (Unselfish love)

During a radio competition came the question: What is the most beautiful thing a woman can have said to her?

After much discussion a young woman received the first prize. 'The most beautiful thing a woman can get to hear,' she thought, 'is when the baby starts crying at three in the morning and her husband says: Stay in bed. I'll go!'

---

92. How is benevolent love true love of neighbour?

Because it seeks another's good and not one's own.

The wildest drive of my life

The well-known racing driver Hans Stuck has this to tell:

I was going to the Cuneo race in Italy. My mechanic and I were driving in my private car along the Montreux-St Maurice motorway making for Martigny. Not far from St Maurice a detachment of soldiers came towards us signalling to us: sizeable landslide − motorway blocked for days. To reach Italy there had to be a detour of 200 kilometres.

In Ollon we had to stop again on account of a small group of people in the middle of the road, gesticulating, shouting, wringing their hands. We asked the cause of the excitement. A very young woman turned to me weeping.

'I must be in Turin within six hours. I've fetched the serum from Berlin that's not to be had in Turin − but it must be in the doctor's hands by midnight. Otherwise it will be too late. There's no airplane to be had. And a car won't make it. . .'

The poor woman was incoherent with worry. Her anxiety was for the life of her child.

141

'Get in, lady,' I said. 'I'm going to Turin anyway — and if all goes well you'll be home with the serum at 11.45.'

I didn't myself believe what I said. My companion secretly glanced at his watch: 6.00 p.m. We had to put behind us 412 kilometres over the Great St Bernard — taking into account an average of 60 kilometres, scarcely possible in the mountains, and we needed something like seven hours — so that meant 12.45 in Turin. We sped off. A word was exchanged now and again, and the odd sentence. Mesmerised, our passenger stared at the clock on the Dashboard. Three, four times the traffic police signalled us to stop. We saw and heard nothing and thundered on at 120 kilometres an hour through villages and streets, through French Switzerland, up to the Great St Bernard.

It was just after 9.00p.m. when we were climbing the first bends of the mountain road. I was not myself. Like in a race. Cut the curves, kept up a speed I wondered at myself. Once, it was 8,000 feet up, we got into a skid on ice and the woman beside me screamed:

'If there's an accident my child will die.'

'If we don't risk it — he certainly will,' I replied mercilessly and stepped on the accelerator.

Up at the top the monks came out to us: 'It's not possible to drive down. The road is not cleared yet.'

'Not possible — but I must.'

And now really began the wildest drive of my life. I did not think we would come out of it alive. Between snowdrifts and iceblocks my black and white 'greyhound' wound groaning and complaining in and out. Often it went askew or even in reverse round the bends. All the time close to coming to a halt. In spite of the cold I felt burning hot, I could hardly breathe.

At 10.45 we were safely down in the valley. Still 120 kilometres to Turin. My brakes, wet from the deep snow, were jamming. But it was all the same to me now. Not looking to right or left down the wonderful Italian roads we went at a speed of 130 kilometres.

Five minutes before the 11.45 deadline we stopped before the woman's door. Her husband and the doctor rushed out to us.

The child was saved. The wildest drive of my life had paid off.

93. What contributes among other things to the well-being of our neighbour?

Security, acceptance and above all the things which lead to eternal salvation.

Well cared for (Security)

In New York a few years ago a dreadful experiment was carried out.

It was in a creche for orphans. Six babies were brought into one room. They were really very well cared for as far as food and attention were concerned but without love. It was to see what effect a loveless treatment had on human development.

They soon saw.

After three months the children were all very ill, wouldn't eat and were always sad and fearful.

A human being needs security in a loving environment.

We all need other people's goodwill to go on living.

Right for once (Acceptance)

When I was still at school there were various subjects I had difficulty with.

But the worst was Latin. The teacher was rather hard on me. He never recognised the efforts I made. He only saw my mistakes. I was in despair and wanted to give up.

Then luckily I had another teacher instead: he was a good old priest who really liked boys.

Once he had me translate. As I by chance translated something right that time he encouraged me at once: 'Yes right,' he said, 'you did that well.'

This remark gave me so much pleasure. From that day I found the courage to go on with my Latin.

A clear direction (Eternal salvation)

In Spain I came across this story:

A wealthy businessman advanced in years had no children.

143

So every year he had his eighteen-year-old nephew Juanito to spend the summer holidays with him.

The boy was not exactly the hard working sort. He thought only of living for the day and thought to himself: 'My uncle is rich. He will certainly provide for me when he comes to die.'

When Juanito dropped hints to this effect the old gentleman promised him: 'Listen, Juanito. In my will I shall give you what is necessary to make a good start in life.' Shortly after that the uncle died of a heart attack. The boy ran full of excitement to the notary to find out what he was getting.

The notary looked out the relevant clause. This is it: 'To my beloved newphew I leave the sum of £1.50 for a pocket catechism so that he does not build his life on sand but on the firm foundation of the truth.'

The old uncle knew that the boy would only get more lazy if he inherited a lot of money. That would certainly not be a good start in life. For this he needed more — a clear direction such as is given briefly and to the point in the catechism.

---

94. Why should I love my neighbour?

Because my neighbour is another human being and a child of God.

Is it right to embrace a leper?

In many countries of Africa and Asia lepers are still shunned by the people. It even happens that they are shut up in camps behind barbed wire.

Raoul Follereau, a great friend and helper of the lepers, entered one such camp. He knew that leprosy is only slightly contagious.

The director accompanied Raoul and his wife through the camp. A leper woman named Stella was introduced as an interesting case. Raoul put out his hand.

But like lightning Stella hid her hands behind her back. 'Not allowed,' she said.

The director was embarrassed. Thereupon Raoul asked him: 'Is it also not allowed to embrace the lepers?'

Taken aback the director answered: 'Such a possibility is not mentioned in our rules.'

'Then it is allowed,' put in Raoul firmly. He heartily embraced the sick woman.

That started it. All the sick wanted to embrace him.

Follereau kept saying: 'I am not a doctor. I cannot cure you. I can only love you, for you are God's children.'

Raoul Follereau travelled thousands of miles all over the world to visit the lepers and help them. He could not have done it alone.

At his golden wedding in 1975 he said: 'The greatest good fortune in my life is my wife. I have not undertaken a journey without her. She went with me to all the leper colonies. If I had gone alone the lepers would have thought: "There's an official coming, an interfering busybody." No, it was just a couple with outstretched hands. Straight away my wife took an interest in the children. Then the mothers smiled and when the men saw their women smiling they came as well.'

---

95. How can I love my neighbour as myself?

By treating my neighbour as I would like to be treated.

Not always married

A mother tells this story:

My five-year-old son asked me a short while ago:

'What do people say when they get married?'

'They promise to love each other and be nice to each other.'

After a short pause he said:
'But you're not *always* married, Mummy – or. . .?'

---

96. How should I speak about others?

Speak about the good characteristics of others, not their failings.

The plucked hen

Philip Neri was a shrewd saint. Once he wanted to cure a woman of her unkind talk about others.

He asked her to buy a hen for him at the market. And he told her to pluck the hen on the way back. It was a very windy day.

When the woman brought the hen to Philip Neri the saint complimented her and added:

'Now please leave the hen here and fetch me the feathers.'

'That is impossible,' cried the woman. 'The wind has blown them in all directions.'

Thereupon the saint said very seriously: 'And it is just as impossible to put right the bad things you say about people.'

97. Why should we not judge our neighbour?

Because God alone sees the heart, and we are easily mistaken.

You're a cheat!

It was the summer of 1956. I was a soldier in North Africa. France was waging a colonial war at the time.

It was fairly hard going, especially because of the unbearable heat in that desert region. So we were often off sick. One day I was hit and for a short time completely knocked out. I couldn't breathe. It only lasted a few minutes but my comrades thought: Now it's all up with him. They called the doctor on the radio.

About an hour later they were called out on a job. After assuring themselves that I was somewhat better they all went off and left me alone.

In the evening the army doctor came after a long journey of 200 kilometres. He found me on my feet as I was already feeling better. He was mad.

'You're a cheat,' he shouted at me. 'All you want is to go home so you're making out to be sick.'

I was rather taken aback and tried to make him see the truth. But he would have none of it.

I was very upset to be taken for a liar.

There you see how important it is to judge no one lightly. We should far rather follow the advice of St Francis de Sales: 'Even if a matter has a hundred aspects, you should look at it from the best side.'

98. How can I show loving kindness to someone I don't like?

I can often pray: 'Lord, help that person.'

Churchill and Lady Astor

Here is a well-known example of how not to do it.

The first woman to enter Parliament was Lady Astor. She had a sharp tongue but she met her match in Winston Churchill.

Maliciously she said to him once: 'If I were your wife, Mr Churchill, I should poison your coffee!'

To which Winston Churchill replied: 'And if I were indeed your husband, Lady Astor, I would drink it straight off!'

99. Can wealth and advanced weaponry ensure our future?

No. God protects us, but only when we share with those in need.

Pearl Buck

Pearl Buck is famous especially for her novel *The Good Earth*. Daughter of a protestant missionary, she lived many years in China and came to be fond of the Chinese people. She preached the Gospel in China less by her words than by her actions. Listen to this from her reminiscences of China:

Not long married, I lived at the time in a harbour town of Southern China. On one winter morning I heard knocking on my door. I opened it. There stood a woman clad in rags and looking exhausted and starving. She told me that her husband had left her when famine broke out in the North and she was expecting a child. Could I help her? She had no one to turn to.

I can't say I rejoiced over this early caller. I already had enough cares of my own, especially having to care for my frail old father. However, I was able after much thinking to find a solution: to rent an empty hut for her in the Chinese workers' quarters at the back of our house. Mrs Lu — this was the poor woman's name — was overjoyed. I had a good meal taken to her daily from our kitchen. She got well again and soon brought a sturdy youngster into the world.

About six months after the child's birth I was suddenly startled by the sound of machine gun fire. Then I heard an agitated voice: 'The communists are here! They have taken the town and they are now killing all foreigners.'

Our Chinese servants had already fled the house, for anyone who had anything to do with foreigners was suspect. There we were, my old father, my husband, my sister, her children and mine and nowhere to go. The rattle of machine guns was coming nearer. It was in our street already. Soon it would be all up with us.

Suddenly the door flew open and there stood Mrs Lu. 'Come with me at once.' I said she was putting her life in danger if she sheltered foreigners. She would have none of it. We hastened through the garden and took cover in her hut. Through the cracks between the boards we could see a file of drunken soldiers raiding our house and then storming out again in a rage when they found nobody. We were not discovered.

Two days later when the situation was somewhat quieter we were able to get away on an American boat that was in the harbour.

Mrs Lu had saved our lives.

100. What is the greatest proof of love of neighbour?

To give one's life, like Jesus, for another person.

Change places

It happened in 1917, during the Russian Revolution.

One of the most cruel of the revolutionary leaders had been murdered by some unknown person. The communists immediately took a number of innocent people as hostages. They were all lined up against the wall and the command was given: Every tenth man to be shot.

Number nine was an old Orthodox priest, Fr Alexis. Next to him stood a young priest.

The old one did not hesitate. He whispered to his neighbour: 'I am old and have not long to live. Change places. In God's name I will take your place.'

Shortly after, the old priest was gunned down.